Civil Engineering Pro

Seventh edition

Civil Engineering Procedure

Seventh edition

Institution of Civil Engineers

Published by ICE Publishing, One Great George Street, Westminster, London SW1P 3AA.

Full details of ICE Publishing sales representatives and distributors can be found at:
www.icevirtuallibrary.com/info/printbooksales

Fifth edition published 1996
Sixth edition published 2009
Seventh edition published 2015
Reprinted 2016, 2019

Other titles by ICE Publishing:
Initial Professional Development.
HM Steels. ISBN 978-07277-4147-9

www.icevirtuallibrary.com

A catalogue record for this book is available from the British Library

ISBN 978-0-7277-6069-2

Commissioning Editor: Laura Marriott
Production Editor: Linda Paulus
Market Development Executive: Elizabeth Hobson

Cover image: 'Words, Wide Night'. The construction of the Olympic Stadium in Stratford, East London © Jonathan Meuli. Reproduced with permission.

Typeset by Academic + Technical, Bristol
Index created by Nigel d'Auvergne
Printed and bound in Great Britain by CPI Group (UK) Ltd, Croydon CR0 4YY

FSC
www.fsc.org
MIX
Paper from
responsible sources
FSC® C013604

Contents

Preface to the seventh edition

'Dad. What do you teach the students at the university?' asked my 6-year-old son on the way to school one morning. 'Civil engineering' I replied. 'What is civil engineering?' he further enquired. I mused on the fact that we had only 3 minutes between his question and the school gate so brevity was essential. 'Bridges, roads, canals, et cetera' I replied. My son looked at me with his enthusiastic smile and said 'and what else?' Maybe my answer was a little too brief. 'Civil engineering is the art of directing the great sources of power in nature for the use and convenience of man' I proclaimed. My son looked bemused. The answer seemed to satisfy his curiosity though, and he ran off to his class with a skip in his step armed with his new knowledge.

Earlier in the year, my wife, a Girl-Guiding leader, had asked me to accompany her patrol on a trip to a local civil engineering project at Leeds railway station (see Chapter 5 of this book). The trip was part of a 'civil engineering badge' that my wife and her fellow Guider had devised, inspired, no doubt, by the array of construction and civil engineering literature scattered about our home. During the visit, one of the Girl Guides asked the same question that my son had posed. Her response was 'umm, sounds boring' ... 'tell me something exciting about civil engineering.' I mused briefly on the famous Yellow Pages entry 'for Civil Engineering, *see* Boring' before recounting the 2012 Olympics, the Large Hadron Collider, Crossrail, the Channel Tunnel and so on. Then, in a moment of inspiration, I pointed vaguely in the direction of the Pennines and explained to her that the tallest piece of infrastructure in the UK is the Emily Moor television transmission mast, and that it was located right here in Yorkshire. 'Without civil engineering you wouldn't be able to watch your favourite TV programmes!', I asserted. She looked at me and said, 'Huh, TV is boring these days too!'.

Times change rapidly; the construction industry is perhaps one where change tends to be much faster than elsewhere. This updated edition of a text that spans back many decades reflects this dynamic landscape. It emphasises the central role of the discipline in building sustainable economies and stable governments. The target audience remains the same; students of civil engineering and the allied disciplines and those entering professional practice. The text was prepared at a time of major change in the construction sector; the advent of the new CDM 2015 Regulations, the ramp-up to building information modelling (BIM) Level 2 readiness and the 2015 UK General Election, which witnessed significant lobbying by the Institution of Civil Engineers through its 'Manifesto for Infrastructure'.

Academic staff from the Management of Projects' research and teaching group at the University of Manchester School of Mechanical, Aerospace and Civil Engineering have prepared this text, drawing on support and guidance from a group of experienced practitioners. We inherited the text from the Management Panel of the Institution of Civil Engineers and we are grateful to them for providing us with a solid foundation to work from.

The University of Manchester and NEC3 have a strong connection in Martin Barnes CBE, who read for his doctorate at the former University of Manchester Institute for Science and Technology (UMIST) under the supervision of Stephen Wearne. His work demonstrated the value of integrating the project control areas of time, cost and quality, known today as the 'iron triangle'. His research at Manchester led him to pioneer the New Engineering Contract, which is known globally for its unique, project management centric approach to project execution. In our revisions, the most noticeable change is the treatment of the New Engineering Contract, third edition (NEC3), replacing the ICE Conditions of Contract as the endorsed form of the Institution.

Richard Kirkham
Summer 2015

Drafting panel

Chair
Richard Kirkham (University of Manchester)

Panel Members
Ian Besford (Mott Macdonald)
Martin Cook (DQM Solutions Ltd)
Lucia Fullalove (Highways England)
Andrew Gale (University of Manchester)
Stewart Hartley (Lend Lease)
Matthew Kirkham (AECOM)
David Ling (University of Manchester)
Roger Milburn (Arup)
Jack Rostron (J Rostron Solicitors, Chair of the
    Residential Property Tribunal (Wales) and
    member of the First-tier Tribunal (Property
    Chamber) (England))
Peter Schwanethal (PKS International)
Jon Svikis (Mott Macdonald)

Acknowledgements

Chapter 11 of this text is based on the original work of Tobias Olsson, Danny Brand and Anas Bataw. The panel chair gratefully acknowledges Mary Mayall, Carole Hayes, Meera Idris and Gabriella Barnes for their assistance with the final production of this text.

Civil Engineering Procedure
ISBN 978-0-7277-6069-2

http://dx.doi.org/10.1680/cep.60692.001

Chapter 1
Civil engineering projects

A short history of civil engineering

The history of 'civil engineering' in the UK can be traced back to the sixteenth century and the formation of the Smeatonian Society of Civil Engineers in 1771 by John Smeaton FRS (b. 1724, Austhorpe, Leeds; d. 1792). Smeaton's early work on mathematical instrumentation led to his election to the Royal Society in 1753, but he will remain renowned for his work on lighthouse design and, in particular, the third Eddystone Lighthouse, which was constructed using dovetailed blocks of Portland stone, designed to withstand extreme offshore conditions. Smeaton is often referred to as 'the father of civil engineering', and had devised the term 'civil engineering' to differentiate his work from the more common military engineering that prevailed at the time. However, some historians suggest that the Smeatonian Society was as much a 'victualing club' as a technical/learned institution and so it was in 1818 that three young engineers met in London and founded what is today the Institution of Civil Engineers (ICE). It was to become the world's first professional engineering body. The eminent engineer Thomas Telford (b. 1757, Dumfries, Scotland; d. 1834) was elected as the first president in 1820 and by 1828, with the help of Telford's connections, the ICE had secured its first Royal Charter (which was subsequently updated by HM Queen Elizabeth II in 1975) (ICE, 2015). The Charter defined civil engineering as:

> the art of directing the great sources of power in nature for the use and convenience of man, as the means of production and of traffic in states, both for external and internal trade, as applied in the construction of roads, bridges, aqueducts, canals, river navigation and docks for internal intercourse and exchange, and in the construction of ports, harbours, moles, breakwaters and lighthouses, and in the art of navigation by artificial power for the purposes of commerce, and in the construction and application of machinery, and in the drainage of cities and towns.

The ICE had much work to do in promoting the profession of engineering. Most practicing engineers were in the armed forces but the election of Telford was significant in attracting membership and building the learned society that is the ICE today. Telford's influence in the UK is significant; his work involved all manner of infrastructure projects, from churches to castles, canals to harbours, tunnels to bridges. He was also given the nickname 'the Colossus of Roads' because his designs were used to construct all major British highways (during his lifetime he built over 1000 miles of roads).

Telford, Isambard Kingdom Brunel (b. 1806, Portsmouth; d. 1859, London) and Smeaton are, perhaps, the most well-known civil engineers of our time. In 2007, and to reflect the ongoing modernisation of the profession, the Council of the ICE adopted a new definition:

Civil engineering is a vital art, working with the great sources of power in nature for the wealth and well-being of the whole of society. Its essential feature is the exercise of imagination to engineer the products and processes, and develop the people needed to create and maintain a sustainable natural and built environment. It requires a broad understanding of scientific principles, a knowledge of materials and the art of analysis and synthesis. It also requires research, team-working, leadership and business skills. A civil engineer is one who practices all or part of this art. (NCE, 2007)

Clearly, the concept of 'sustainable' refers not only to environmental and social considerations, but also to the need to maintain an ongoing, safe, secure and reliable provision of transport, utilities and other infrastructure, which are essential for the economy, business and the growing population to thrive. This means providing capacity and supplies at a reasonable level, in balance with the current and projected levels of investment required, and ultimately the nation's ability to pay, whether through direct charges or taxation. This has become the core consideration of many of today's largest infrastructure owners, who recognise that civil engineering entails more than discrete projects. This book focuses on procedure for projects, and readers are provided with initial references to the wider context of infrastructure asset management. Sustainability in its widest sense, in civil engineering, was addressed most eloquently by HRH Prince Charles when he addressed the ICE in 2012.

Today, the ICE has over 86 000 members across Europe, the Americas, Africa, the Middle East and the Asia-Pacific region. The Institution is composed of many special interest groups and committees, which span the range of technical disciplines across civil engineering: geotechnics, coastal engineering, energy and buildings, to name but a few. This book, *Civil Engineering Procedure* seventh edition, supports the work of the 'Professional Practice' group of the ICE and is concerned with issues around project management, health and safety, contracts and procurement, and ethics. In Chapters 4 and 6 of this book, the use of modern forms of contract to support the delivery of complex infrastructure schemes will be introduced; the most notable being the New Engineering Contract (NEC). NEC changed the way in which civil engineering projects are delivered, and focuses on project management, collaboration and good risk management. The contract has been used on a number of iconic projects, such as Crossrail, the Velodrome built for the London Olympic Games in 2012, and the International Criminal Court in The Hague, the Netherlands. It is therefore appropriate that this first chapter outlines the basic fundamentals of projects and project management.

Projects

A project is defined in BS 6079-1 (BSI, 2010) as 'a unique set of co-ordinated activities, with definite start and finishing points, undertaken by an individual or organisation to meet specific objectives within defined schedule, cost and performance parameters'. This definition highlights a number of important considerations in the context of civil engineering projects. First and foremost, projects are fundamentally different from processes and procedures (these activities usually result in the same or similar outcomes over a number of times). Their transient nature is an important distinction, but there are a number of other 'principal features' that characterise projects (BS 6079-1):

- Their duration is usually predetermined (finite), with definite start and end dates.
- What happens during the undertaking of a project invariably affects the subsequent events, both inside and outside the organisation.
- The project organisation is often temporary and can sometimes change through the project life cycle.
- All projects are undertaken in an environment of risk and uncertainty.
- Projects are seldom carried out in isolation and can often interact with other projects and organisational entities.

The project life cycle

The project life cycle depicted in BS 6079-1 is characterised by a series of 'generic' phases and milestones (Figure 1.1). These shall be examined in more detail later in this book, but it is important to note here that the British Standard has been adapted to suit the specific needs of the construction industry. Notable examples include:

- the Royal Institute of British Architects (RIBA) *Plan of Work* (RIBA, 2013) (for building projects)
- Governance of Railway Infrastructure Projects (GRIP) (Network Rail, 2014) (for railway infrastructure projects)
- the *Project Control Framework Handbook* (Highways Agency, 2013) (for Highways England schemes).

Projects can vary in scale, complexity, degree of innovation, urgency and duration; the magnitudes of which have implications for programme (how the activities will be sequenced), schedule (how long the activities will take) and cost.

3

Figure 1.1 The life cycle of a civil engineering project

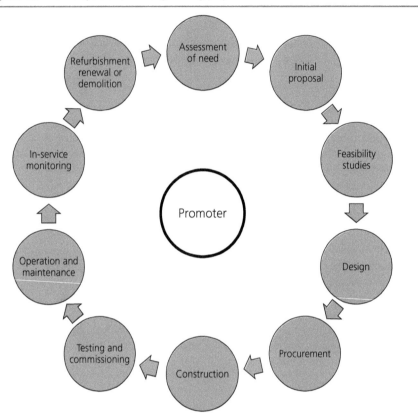

The durations of the life cycle stages vary from project to project, sometimes with delays between one and the next. Figure 1.1 shows the common sequence of these stages. It is important to note that phases are not necessarily discrete and sequential; the method of procurement (see Chapters 4 and 6) may lead to overlaps, particularly in the case of unexpected, urgent or accelerated projects.

Concept

The cycle starts with a concept or an initial proposal to meet a 'brief'. The concept, combined with engineering ideas, experience and records from previous projects, together with information from research indicating problems to address, new opportunities, provide the basis for subsequent evaluation. The relative importance of information from research, demand, experience and records depends upon the extent of novelty of the proposal and how far innovation will be required in its design, but all these sources of information are always relevant to some extent.

Feasibility

If the concept appears viable, the project proceeds to 'feasibility studies', where possible solutions are explored in greater detail. Several alternative options likely to meet the brief are usually considered. In unexpected, urgent or accelerated projects, this stage is often compressed or even omitted. If the project is urgent, little time is spent in trying to optimise the proposal. More commonly, alternatives have to be evaluated in order to decide whether to proceed and how best to do so. This is particularly important from an economic, regulatory and environmental perspective. (Note: The term 'promote' is used in the rest of this book to indicate the particular promotor, employer or client for a project.)

The results of early feasibility studies may require the promoter to reconsider the original concept. If so, the proposal will be refined further. It is at this stage that the promoter may revise the brief in light of new information, changing stakeholder requirements or legislative/planning issues. This process is iterative and can take some considerable time and is almost always a feature of more complex civil engineering projects. Decisions taken at this stage can, however, have a significant impact on the 'whole-life' costs (WLCs) of the project (Figure 1.2), and major promoters are now requiring WLC comparisons between options as part of this decision-making and at subsequent stages.

Figure 1.2 Project cost versus opportunity to influence cost

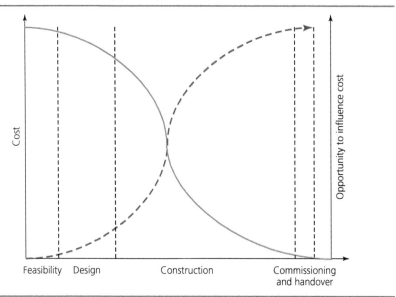

Feasibility   Design   Construction   Commissioning
                                                    and handover

The investigation of civil engineering schemes and their subsequent evaluation is often a non-linear process because of the inherent risk and uncertainty of the data and information available to the project team at any one time. The promoter will usually seek professional project management/cost planning advice at this stage to help understand the risks of construction and operation, future prices of materials, equipment, labour, and other resources, and the likely operating performance and user demand and behaviour, etc. A range of financial, socio-economic, environmental and other evaluation methods are used at this stage to assist with the decision-making process. Discounted cash flow and/or social cost–benefit techniques are often used, usually expressed in terms of net present value (NPV) as these enable comparison of various options, taking into account costs and benefits using discount rates to reflect the timing during a project's economic life when particular costs and benefits arise.

Quantifying the benefits is particularly difficult in cases where a capital project will not generate a revenue stream, for instance a project to reduce accidents at a junction on a road. In the UK, HM Treasury sets out rules to guide the appraisal of such projects. Nevertheless, a specification, budget and programme are normally decided, together with contingency, schedule, programme and sources of funding. As the decisions made at this stage define the scope and standards of the project they will form the basis of all that is to follow.

Project selection

The investigations and feasibility studies of a proposed project may take some considerable time. This can be for reasons including engineering complexity, planning and legal issues, as well as environmental impact concerns. The conclusions will either be selection or rejection of the proposed project. This decision effectively determines the project's future. Sufficient time and resources should therefore be used to ensure that the decision is sound and transparent. If the proposed project is rejected, it could be revived at a later date if new information is obtained, or priorities and evaluation criteria change, or if a new design and other ideas prove to be acceptable. The information used for the feasibility studies should, therefore, have been of sufficient quality to enable the optimum decision to be made. Similarly, if a proposal is selected, the information used should have been good enough to ensure a successful start to the project. A range of methodologies are available to support project selection. One commonly used approach is cost–benefit analysis (CBA), usually incorporating a discounting of cost and benefits over time, with the evaluation result often expressed as a net present value (NPV). However, other techniques such as multi-criteria decision analysis, or purely financial discounted cash-flow assessments may also be used, depending on the context and nature of the project. If the project is selected and sanctioned the activities change from assessing whether it should proceed to deciding how best it should be realised and to specifying what needs to be done.

Design

The decisions made early in the project life cycle have a significant impact on the time, cost, quality, safety, operational effectiveness, social and economic impacts, and eventual decommissioning of a project, and therefore on its ultimate success. Design ideas are often the start of possible projects. The main design stage of deciding how to use materials and control systems, the methods of construction, installation, operation and maintenance required, and the safety aspects to be considered to realise the project usually follows, as indicated in Figure 1.1. The products of design are calculations, drawings and a specification; often accompanied by an estimate of the quantities of materials, a schedule of construction activities or an estimate of costs; and possibly by a manual advising on operating and maintenance requirements; although only a sketch may be needed for a very small project, repairs or maintenance work.

Intermediate stages of design may be needed to provide sufficient detail to check estimates of costs and provide a scheme for approval by the promoter and statutory authorities. On a novel project, further research and development work may be needed to investigate new or risky problems before the project is continued.

On complex projects, the use of early contractor involvement (ECI) is an increasingly common means of achieving economies through improved synthesis of design and construction processes.

Contracts

Figure 1.1 indicates that a contract for construction follows the completion of the design stage. This is normal in the traditional procurement model for civil engineering and building projects in the UK. Alternatively, an outline design or performance requirement can be the basis of a contract and the chosen contractor then becomes responsible for detailed design and construction; this is often described as 'design and build' (see Chapters 4 and 6 where the various styles of contract governing relationships between the promoter and the contractor are discussed further). Consultants, designers, project managers, the supply chain and others are usually also employed under contracts; some of them from the start of the investigation of a proposed project.

Construction

The construction phase usually requires the largest resource input to a project in the periods prior to handover and operation, as is shown in the classic 's-curve' in Figure 1.2. It is essential at this stage to monitor and control costs through effective project management. New forms of contract, such as the NEC (see later chapters), emphasise this by providing mechanisms to support collaboration, communication and a shared vision for planning, organisation, health, safety and cost control. Demolition and substantial

7

changes to existing structures, which may be needed at various stages in a project's life-cycle, and dealing with complex or unexpected ground conditions require special care and will often require a particular form of contract to reflect the risks and uncertainties that work of this kind presents.

Most companies and public bodies that promote projects employ contractors from this stage on to carry out the physical work on site. There is now a growing tendency by the promoter to seek ECI or to obtain construction expertise through the appointment of a construction manager through the design phase. Alternatively, contractors who take on the role of project promoters are normally fully responsible for design; for instance when investing in the construction of a building for sale or financing an infrastructure project through a public private partnership (PPP). For virtually all construction situations, the contractors will, in turn, employ specialist and local sub-contractors to work on site and provide services, plant, materials and sub-systems.

Testing, commissioning and handover
Project completion is usually achieved when any outstanding works are completed and the final account is agreed with the contractor. This is usually described as 'practical completion' and the contract administrator will issue a certificate to that effect. Following practical completion, the contractor will be required to make good any defects that have been identified during the handover, and in subsequent operation over a specified period of time. Unless the construction contract also includes a maintenance requirement associated with on-going operations, this time period is defined in the contract and is typically 52 weeks. NEC3 contracts, the liability to make good any defects relates to those identified before the 'defects date' established in the contract, and such defects must be remedied within a defined 'defects correction period' that starts from the time when the defect is notified to the contractor.

This stage can often be quite challenging, particularly during commissioning where 'teething' problems may occur.

Assets in service
The subsequent operation and maintenance, refurbishment, renewal, replacement of equipment or services, decommissioning and demolition are increasingly considered under an asset management strategy and asset management plan. These may well include various small or medium separate projects over the life cycle, which should each proceed through an appropriate sequence of investigations and decisions as described in Figure 1.1. The full asset life cycle is described in the ICE's *Guiding Principles of Asset Management* (2014), which itself contains a useful bibliography.

Objectives

Each stage in the cycle shown in Figure 1.1 should be planned and managed effectively so as to provide a sound basis for a successful project. The nature of the construction industry, the inherent risk, uncertainty and complexity associated with civil engineering projects and the transient nature of project teams, changing promoter requirements and the wider economy, create a dynamic environment that does not lend itself to a precisely sequential and process-oriented approach. Nevertheless, the purpose of the whole sequence, however iterative it may be, should be to produce a successful project. The following chapters of this book describe how each stage of a project can be organised to achieve this result.

REFERENCES AND FURTHER READING

BSI (2010) BS 6079-1. Guide to project management: British Standard, Part 1: Project management. BSI, London, UK.

HA (Highways Agency) (2013) *The Project Control Framework Handbook*, v2.

HRH Prince Charles (2012) A speech by HRH The Prince of Wales at the 2012 Institution of Civil Engineers Halcrow Lecture. http://www.nce.co.uk/new-definition-for-civil-engineering/212786.article (accessed 29 September 2015).

ICE (2015) The History of the Institution of Civil Engineers. https://www.ice.org.uk/ (accessed 12 August 2015).

ICE (2014) Realising a world class infrastructure. ICE Guiding Principles of Asset Management. https://www.ice.org.uk/getattachment/disciplines-and-resources/best-practice/realising-a-world-class-infrastructure/Guiding-Principles-of-Asset-Management.pdf.aspx (accessed 12 August 2015).

NCE (*New Civil Engineer*) (2007) New Definition for Civil Engineering. NCE, 31 October. http://www.nce.co.uk/new-definition-for-civil-engineering/212786.article (accessed 29 September 2015).

Network Rail (2014) Governance for Rail Infrastructure Projects (GRIP) Policy Standard (NR/L1/INI/PM/GRIP/100).

Royal Institute of British Architects (RIBA) (2013) *The RIBA Plan of Work*. RIBA Publishing, London, UK.

Civil Engineering Procedure
ISBN 978-0-7277-6069-2

Chapter 2
Concept and promotion of a civil engineering project

Project promoters

The promoters of civil engineering projects vary widely in their legal status. This is an important consideration when seeking to understand the impacts of planning legislation, funding, project governance and control. Promoters come in 'all shapes and sizes', from large central, regional and local government organisations (and their associated agencies), to limited liability companies, joint-venture partnerships and individuals. Other legally incorporated or unincorporated bodies may also be promoters: charities, passenger transport executives (i.e. Metro in West Yorkshire, CENTRO in the West Midlands), waste disposal authorities and police and crime commissioners are all examples.

The advent of public private partnerships (PPPs), and the private finance initiative (PFI) in particular, has brought about a new form of project participant, the special purpose company (SPC). SPCs are created from a mixture of promoter types, including contracting organisations, financial institutions and individual investors.

Central government

Consultancy, construction and any other work undertaken for UK government departments and agencies is paid for, ordinarily, out of funds from HM Treasury. The budget is determined by Parliament and any expenditure in excess of the voted amount, although it may be authorised by a department or agency, requires a supplementary vote. The government then authorises its various departments and agencies to proceed with projects and studies for possible projects.

Contractors are not under any obligation to enquire whether or not the department or agency is contracting beyond the funds voted by Parliament. The government is bound by a contract made on its behalf by any of its departments or other agents that have the authority to enter into that contract.

It should be noted that in situations where projects are commissioned under either PPP or PFI arrangements, initial finance is provided by the private sector. The private sector then typically receives payments from Government or other public sector bodies against performance criteria during the operational phase of the contract (known as the concession period), as opposed to the traditional capital payment for the construction, as works progress.

Local government
The powers of local authorities in the UK are stated in their Charters, in Acts of Parliament constituting them and under general or special Acts governing their procedures and applications of funds. Local authorities can enter into contracts and raise funds for payments due under these Acts and Charters. A contract validly entered into carries an implied undertaking that the authority possesses or will collect the requisite funds.

Local authorities are subject to the ordinary legal liabilities as to their powers to contract and their liability to be sued. Lack of funds is no defence to a legal action for payment. For example, a local authority's liability in a contract to pay for work will not be cancelled by the refusal of a government department to provide a grant or to authorise the expenditure.

Statutory authorities
The powers of statutory authorities are stated in the various Acts of Parliament constituting them (for example, the Environment Act 1995 (as amended) establishes the Environment Agency and the Scottish Environment Protection Agency, both major promoters of civil engineering projects in the UK). The legal position of such bodies and of their officials is similar to that of local authorities. Former public utilities (e.g. water, gas and electricity) and nationalised industries which have been privatised (e.g. British Steel) are now incorporated companies.

Incorporated companies
Under English law, an incorporated company can enter into contracts within the purposes of its memorandum of association or within the powers prescribed by any special Act of Parliament incorporating the company or any other Act granting it powers for a specific purpose.

Special purpose companies (SPCs)
SPC is a term used to describe an organisation formed to undertake a specific project (or series of projects). It can be created as a distinct and separate legal entity. It is usually formed of companies who have a common interest in the delivery of privately funded contracts and will typically include contractors and their strategic partners and stakeholders, for example key manufacturers, operators, designers and funders.

Typically, a new company will be created to act as the concession company for the project, with the stakeholders having agreed their share and contribution in the formation of the company. Although the shareholding capital in the SPC may be limited, the terms of an SPC concession will be such as to make the stakeholders jointly and severally liable to the promoter for costs/losses in the event of default for whatever reason of one or more of the members of the SPC. The contractual and legal arrangements are complex, particularly as the construction of the works is undertaken by various members of the SPC, but all have liabilities to it!

Other bodies

A person or persons who are not a trading corporation, for instance a charity, can be the promoter of a project. A consultant or contractor invited to enter into a contract with such a promoter should check the authority of one or more of the individuals involved to commit the rest in personal liability for the purpose of that contract and for making payments due under it. The safest course for other parties is to enter into a contract with a sufficient number of members of the body to ensure that their collective financial status is adequate.

Overseas

The legal status of companies and of government bodies and the legal controls of construction vary from country to country, even within the Commonwealth or the European Union (EU). Ascertaining the status and authority of promoters and others overseas needs local expertise (Loraine, 1991). Experience and advice are also usually needed on the culture and customs of construction organisations and individuals.

The World Bank, United Nations Industrial Development Organization, Asian Development Bank, European Investment Bank, European Bank for Reconstruction and Development and other funding agencies provide the finance for some civil engineering projects. Finance is also made available directly to poorer countries by the more wealthy countries, usually through government departments, for example the Department for International Development (in the UK) and development authorities in the country where a project is to be built.

Study team

Many industrial companies and government bodies employ their own engineering and other professional staff on the first studies and evaluation of projects. They also employ consultants, as do most smaller or occasional promoters. The promoter usually enters into a contract (service agreement) for the consultant's services.

Many large traditional construction consulting engineering practices have become 'multi-disciplinary', being able to provide a range of services beyond their historical function in a more traditional role. Similarly, other project management consultancies have expanded the other way and are able to offer specialist engineering services as part of their portfolio. Such consultants are often badged as a 'one-stop shop', saving the promoter from engaging a number of individual specialist consultancies.

Consulting engineer

In traditional civil engineering in the UK, the promoter employs a consulting engineer to investigate and report on a proposed project. The consulting engineer may be a firm or an individual, depending on the size and risks of the project. The consulting engineer's role at this stage of a project is to provide engineering and other associated advice to enable the promoter to assess its feasibility and the relative merits of various alternative schemes to meet his or her requirements. Other specialist consultants may be needed, in a team operating under a lead consultant.

Project sponsor

Many promoters are organisations within which departments are employed on various functions, such as the operation or maintenance of existing facilities, planning future needs, personnel management, finance, legal services and public relations. All these will have some interest in proposed projects, but they have different expertise and may have different objectives and priorities for each project.

A promoter should therefore make one senior manager responsible for defining the objectives and priorities of a proposed project. It is the role of sponsor or 'project champion'. The role is not necessarily a separate one. It is logically part of the responsibilities of the manager who has the authority to ensure that sufficient resources are employed at this stage.

Project manager

Projects are complex. There is a recognition that efficiencies can be made in the construction process through effective programme management, i.e. the undertaking of a series of individual projects under one umbrella and, similarly, in the management of buildings, land and other facilities that comprise an organisation's estate.

Political, commercial, legal and technical change is such that specialists are needed to advise on the best way to develop and promote particular types of project. In addition, the general public will expect to be consulted on major projects or projects which may affect the environment and quality of local life. This will be done through the appropriate planning legislation, including for example The Infrastructure Act (2015) and The Town and Country Planning Act 1990. In these circumstances the promoter's interests may be best served by the appointment of one person, or an external organisation on a complex project, to plan and manage the project and coordinate relationships with other organisations. The role of the project manager (this role is referred to as the 'promoter's manager' in some contracts) is particularly important for

- ensuring that the project objectives are drafted for agreement by the promoter and relevant financial or statutory authorities
- advising on stakeholder relationships
- obtaining advice on the likely cost of the project, and possible sources of finance
- planning for site selection and acquisition
- planning for public consultation, a planning application and representation at public inquiries
- preparing and coordinating the project strategy or 'brief'
- developing the project procurement strategy
- planning for the appointment of the larger team and the systems and so on, needed for the life of the project.

Programme management encapsulates a wider role and introduces much greater emphasis on programming and logistics management, and may by undertaken in the role of a delivery partner within an integrated project team. Such arrangements are now used for complex projects where the promoter is not fully conversant in the procurement and delivery of construction works, for example an airport operator or rail franchisee.

In addition to the project manager role, a programme manager may be responsible for

- overall control of the project delivery – milestone management
- the introduction and management of core processes
- budget control
- the balance of time, cost and quality considerations.

Estate management is often referred to as portfolio management and may be undertaken by firms specialising in facilities management (FM) or by multi-disciplinary firms with FM capability. Promoters will generally set the requirements for repairs and refurbishment programmes, undertaken as 'hard' FM, with maintenance of services, contracts for cleaning, and so on, known as 'soft' FM. Projects may be for one or the other or both.

Services provided by the project manager or an outside organisation for portfolio management may include:

- advising and preparing the project objectives schedules
- negotiations with stakeholders
- development of the planned maintenance regime
- arrangements for unplanned maintenance
- letting and management of various contracts
- project controls
- financial reporting.

Once a project has been sanctioned, the project manager, or the external organisation, needs the authority of the promoter to manage and control its design and construction. The role of project manager is also not necessarily a job separate from other work, depending upon the size, risks and importance of a project. Due to the amount of time it demands, it is usually separate from the role of the senior manager who is the project sponsor. The project manager may be the consulting engineer appointed to investigate and report on the proposed project. Alternatively, the project manager may be an employee of the promoter or a specialist company in project management.

Selection of the team
Selection of a consulting engineer
The selection of a consulting engineer should start with defining the expertise appropriate to the project. Corporate membership of the Institution of Civil Engineers (ICE) is recognised as the appropriate qualification for positions of responsibility in civil engineering. Corporate members of the ICE comprise Members, who have appropriate education, training and experience, and Fellows, who are senior members who have held positions of major responsibility on important engineering work for some years. All are subject to the ICE's by-laws, regulations and rules of professional conduct. Consulting engineers traditionally practised in partnerships, but increasingly these operate as limited liability companies, which may be multi-disciplinary in nature.

Advice for promoters regarding suitable consulting engineers and their methods of engagement and working can be obtained from the Association for Consultancy and Engineering (formerly known as the Association of Consulting Engineers). A formal agreement (a contract) should be completed between promoter and consulting engineer, which sets out the duties and responsibilities of each party and the fees and expenses to be paid. The terms of employment of a consulting engineer need to be consistent with those of others employed on a project, for instance the project manager, where the project manager is a separate organisation from that of the promoter and contractors. Sets of model terms are available for the employment of most professions. Example terms for consulting engineers and project managers are listed in Appendix A.

Overseas
Engineers working overseas must be prepared to adapt to different laws, cultures, contractual arrangements, professional standards and terms of employment. In some overseas countries, an engineer may practise only if registered for that purpose. In the USA, licensure (registration) for the engineering and surveying professions is regulated by each individual state. Only licensed engineers can call themselves 'professional engineers' (PEs) and perform certain tasks. The titles 'engineer', 'civil engineer' and others are protected in most states (unlike in the UK). However, the titles chartered engineer (CEng) and ICE member (MICE) are not legally recognised and cannot be used as an alternative to PE.

Selection of a project manager

The project manager should be appropriately qualified and have adequate experience of the type of project and the duties and responsibilities that the promoter intends to assign to them as the manager of the project. Membership of the Association for Project Management (MAPM) is the recognised base qualification for project managers. A project manager for a civil engineering project usually needs to have the expertise to advise on risk management, project planning, contracts and organising design and construction, and often holds a professional qualification from an institution such as the ICE. The individual may also need the financial expertise to advise the promoter on the expected whole-life cost of the project, cash flow and alternative sources of finance, or have access to this from others in his or her organisation. An understanding of other professions may therefore be important for the project manager, particularly during the process of setting up a project team to manage a large and complex project.

The selection of the project manager – be it an individual or a specialist organisation – should follow closely the process outlined for the selection of a consulting engineer. The promoter can obtain advice on this from the Association for Consultancy and Engineering and the Association for Project Management (APM). Increasingly, the promoters of civil engineering and other projects are employing project managers whose competence has been certified by the APM or an equivalent organisation, such as the Project Management Institute.

Selection of the project team

The project manager of a large or complex project will require engineering and other assistance. It is normal practice for the project manager to select and appoint the project team, but in some instances the promoter may appoint the team on the advice of a specialist project management organisation. The selection and appointment of the team should be based on the same criteria as those applied in the selection of the consulting engineer, and care must be taken to appoint a team that will have the expertise and the resources needed for the project.

Preparation of brief

Responsibilities

An important task for the project manager is to ensure that the promoter defines the objectives for the project and agrees a project brief to guide the next stage of work. The brief should state

- the promoter's objectives and priorities
- how consultants and other resources are to be employed
- an outline programme and budget, setting dates and cost targets for the investigations and design studies needed for the feasibility study.

The brief should be designed to guide the investigation and evaluation of alternative policies and engineering schemes which appear on initial consideration to meet the promoter's needs. An example of this would be a brief to investigate solutions to ease the traffic problems in a congested town. There may be several types of options, for example: a by-pass, traffic calming measures, provision of park-and-ride facilities, or improved local public transport services. For each of these, alternatives are likely to exist, such as acceptable alternative routes for a bypass and often within these further alternatives such as a tunnel or bridge crossing a river. Cost–benefit studies, risk analyses and environmental impact assessments for each alternative will help to concentrate the choice down to two or three alternatives which meet the criteria set by the promoter.

Considerable investigative work may be needed to reach a decision on which of the alternatives merit further evaluation. Sometimes, a short study backed up by site visits and the use of already existing geological, hydrological and other information will be sufficient, together with the consulting engineer's experience on similar projects in the past.

Outline programme and budget

If a date for completion of the project has been set by the promoter, the outline programme should show a time limit for reporting back and for consequent decisions by the promoter, dates for starting design, placing contracts and starting construction. The programme should also show any dates critical for financial and statutory approvals and agreements by others.

The basis is now established for the next stage, the investigation of the proposed project and reporting the results and recommendations to the promoter.

FURTHER READING AND REFERENCES

Griffith A and King A (2003) *Best Practice Tendering for Design and Build Projects*. Thomas Telford, London, UK.

Hamilton A (2001) *Managing Projects for Success*. Thomas Telford, London, UK.

Kamara JM, Anumba CJ and Evbuomwan NF (2002) *Capturing Client Requirements in Construction Projects*. Thomas Telford, London, UK.

Loraine RK (1991) *Construction Management in Developing Countries*. Thomas Telford, London, UK.

Civil Engineering Procedure
ISBN 978-0-7277-6069-2

ICE Publishing: All rights reserved
http://dx.doi.org/10.1680/cep.60692.019

Chapter 3
Feasibility

Introduction

The feasibility stage of the project life cycle is concerned with establishing the need for the project, the objectives, any constraints and the options available to achieve the objectives, with the ultimate aim of determining a recommendation for a preferred option.

The scope and rigour of a feasibility study depends on the size, complexity and risk associated with the project, as well as the amount of work that may have been previously undertaken. Feasibility studies for major infrastructure projects in the UK, such as Crossrail and High Speed 1, and the proposals for a new runway at Heathrow Airport and the proposed High Speed 2 rail line, all feature lengthy and sophisticated procedures. It is not unknown for feasibility studies to take decades. Feasibility studies are often undertaken by specialist consultancies with expertise in social research methods and planning.

Confirming the need

The reason the project is needed may be clear, for example additional accommodation for an expanding company. Often, though, part of the feasibility study is to confirm this need, enabling clear objectives to be set against which alternatives can be evaluated.

One way to demonstrate the project's need is to consider the '*do nothing*' option. Understanding the consequences of carrying on with the current situation can often highlight exactly why the project is required.

While the consequences may be self-evident, they should be assessed objectively and quantified where appropriate. This will involve collation of the relevant information, which may be a substantial piece of work in its own right. Predicting future demand might be part of the feasibility study or may make use of existing forecasts. In the examples in Table 3.1, the water company would need to have a clear idea of the current water quality in order to specify the correct treatment process. This would be established through laboratory analysis of a series of water samples. The developer promoter investing in his or her property may predict the future rental potential of that particular office block by referring to market trend analysis or making comparison with similar

Table 3.1 Categories of project needs, examples and the consequences of doing nothing

Need	Example	Consequence of doing nothing
Statutory obligations	A water company upgrading a sewage treatment works to meet water quality standards	Fines for non-compliance, loss of reputation
Meeting new demand	An energy company constructing a new power station	Inability to meet demand leading to loss of market share
Achieving a return on the investment made	A property developer refurbishing an office block	Depreciation of the property and reduction in potential lease value

refurbished properties in the area. Quantifying the need for the project helps forecast the benefits it is expected to achieve and establish a business case for carrying out the work.

Establish objectives

Once the need for doing the project is clear, a set of objectives for the project can be established. This determines the criteria against which the success of the project can be measured. These include budgetary, programme, scope, quality and performance objectives. It is important that members of the team producing the feasibility study are clear about what is being considered and manage the promoter's expectations about what the project is expected to achieve.

Budgetary

The budget available for the project will often be the determining factor when considering how to achieve the project's objectives. This can depend on the mechanisms available for financing and funding the project, and the level of risk the promoter is willing to take on, or those financing the project are willing to accept. It is also important to consider any cash flow objectives, such as maintaining a positive balance.

Programme

The time by which the project needs to be completed is usually, although not always, a key objective. For instance, constructing a new stadium for an Olympic Games has a clear end date, but the deadline for constructing a new airport runway may be less tangible and will relate to transport capacity in other locations and forecasts of future demand.

Scope

It is important to agree the scope of the project in broad terms at an early stage. This helps to avoid ambiguity later on, when it is much more costly or reputationally damaging to change what has already been designed or committed to, perhaps when land or property has been acquired and especially when construction has started and things have been built.

Quality and performance

The project's service objectives can be considered in two, often interrelated, ways: quality and performance. Quality objectives define the standards expected and can often refer to industry standards in order to guarantee the adequacy of the completed work. An example would be the design of a bridge's structural elements to recognised international standards. However, such standards do not always guarantee the project will meet the promoter's needs. Perform-ance objectives are used to define the parameters that are really important to the promoter and are often related to capacity. For instance, performance objectives for the replacement of an ageing motorway bridge could include the ability to carry peak rush hour traffic for the next 50 years and have 30% less maintenance costs than the existing bridge.

Identify constraints

Part of the feasibility study is to define the range of factors that will affect the project. Establishing the constraints that exist allows uncertainty to be reduced and the project's risk to be managed. These factors typically include:

- access to the site
- availability of utilities (water, sewerage, electricity, gas, telecommunications)
- risk of flooding
- physical properties of the ground
- composition of waste expected from the site, for example from demolition and excavation, including any contaminated land
- suitability of existing infrastructure for reuse
- ecological/environmental constraints, including the interest of protected species
- whether the site is of archaeological, historical or architectural interest
- rights of ownership, use or access to the land, which would cover both various types of tenancy or lease and such rights as way leaves and easements
- statutory approvals, for example planning permission and building regulations
- unusual, complex or significant health and safety concerns.

These factors are established through a combination of desktop studies of existing records, site inspections and specially commissioned investigations, including explora-tory boreholes to establish soil conditions and environmental impact assessments. As some of these items will have a long lead-time in relation to the time available for the feasibility study, starting to gather information is normally one of the first activities to be done. The scope of the investigations will depend on the time and budget available for the study, and the level of risk the promoter is willing to take on before committing to further development of the project. Where a constraint has not been fully defined, the study should identify the next step that is required.

Stakeholders to the project should be identified during the feasibility study. A common way of establishing a communications strategy for the project is to map the level of parties' interest against the influence they possess. High interest, high influence parties constitute key stakeholders and early engagement with them may be appropriate during the feasibility study. This could include a public consultation.

Investigate and evaluate options

While the identification of constraints may limit the possible solutions, there may well be a number of ways in meeting the project's objectives, each with its own merits. During a feasibility study, each alternative under consideration should have a conceptual design produced to enable its impact on each of the constraints to be assessed and an appropriately robust cost to be estimated. The rigour and detail of the design and cost estimate will be proportional to the novelty of the project and the level of risk the promoter is prepared to take on.

As well as its physical form, the method in which the project is delivered is an important consideration. The involvement of contractors that may carry out the work is often useful in determining the viability of different options, especially when considering methods of construction, buildability and ease of maintenance, which may have a significant bearing on the effectiveness of a solution. Involvement of contractors at this stage needs careful management of expectations and terms of engagement, in order that procurement of the main body of work is not prejudiced. There are likely to be a variety of methods available to procure the project, and their merits should also be considered during the feasibility study. Early engagement of key stakeholders in identifying and evaluating options can provide them with ownership of their aspect of the project.

Evaluation of options by a cost–benefit analysis or other systematic evaluation framework should take into account the full range of project objectives in order to determine the optimum course of action. Where possible, measures should be given to intangible objectives, but it can be difficult to assign meaningful estimates and weighting to subjective or novel aspects. Relative comparison can be used in such cases to rank alternatives.

Future costs and benefits are usually forecast taking into account likely changes during the life of the project, making allowances for uncertainty and expected future changes in relative prices and values. The financial values attached to future costs and benefits are often expressed in terms of current prices, to remove the effects of general price inflation, and can then be discounted over time to take account of the greater value associated with more immediate rather than deferred effects. Discounting applies factors to the value of future costs and benefits that result in those costs and benefits that arise further into the future having their contribution to a project's net present value (NPV) reduced by a greater proportion.

Make recommendation

Following evaluation of the alternative options, the study should be in a position to make a single recommendation. The recommended solution should be summarised in terms of the project's objectives in relation to its advantages over the other options, including the 'do nothing' option and where appropriate a 'do minimum' option, which meets any statutory or regulatory requirements, but represents the least change permissible from the current situation. The proposals should be described in sufficient detail to allow development by other parties. This would include an outline project strategy, including financing and procurement, programme, design and methods of construction. Outstanding areas of uncertainty should be identified as well as the next steps required to mitigate risk. Although there may be the temptation to develop the solution in more detail at this stage, it is prudent to ensure the recommendation is agreed with before proceeding with further work in later stages of the project.

The results of the study will almost certainly be presented to a number of audiences. It can be useful to include a short summary for senior stakeholders who may not have the time to review the full detail. This should identify the need for the project, main objectives, principal constraints, options considered and why the recommended solution was selected.

FURTHER READING AND REFERENCES

Corrie RK (ed.) (1990) *Project Evaluation*. Thomas Telford, London, UK.

Site Investigation Steering Group (2011) *UK Specification for Ground Investigation*, 2nd ed. (Site Investigation in Construction Series). ICE Publishing, London, UK.

Site Investigation Steering Group (2013) *Effective Site Investigation*, 2nd ed. (Site Investigation in Construction Series). ICE Publishing, London, UK.

Smith NJ (1995) *Project Cost Estimating*. Thomas Telford, London, UK.

Civil Engineering Procedure
ISBN 978-0-7277-6069-2

ICE Publishing: All rights reserved
http://dx.doi.org/10.1680/cep.60692.025

Institution of Civil Engineers

publishing

Chapter 4
Project strategy

Scope and purpose

A recommendation to proceed with a project should include proposals for the organisation and management of design, construction and operation/maintenance. This is often referred to as *procurement* – 'the acquisition of goods or services at the best possible price, in appropriate quantity, at the right time and place, etc.'. This definition, drawn from the *Oxford English Dictionary*, reflects the importance of the concepts of time, quality and cost.

In practical terms, procurement is the framework through which the promoter engages with the market and the supply chain to deliver packages of work using one or more contractual instruments, reflecting the appropriate balance of cost, risk and uncertainties that the promoter, contractor and suppliers are willing to bear.

The terms 'procurement' and 'contract' are often used interchangeably; however, there is a distinct difference between these two. Procurement describes the overarching set of activities leading up to acquisition and subsequent ownership and use of an asset. Contracts are a constituent part of the procurement process and set out the legal relationship between two or more of the parties involved.

Project management and control
The project manager

From the start of design the project manager (note: this book assumes that the project manager is externally appointed) should provide central coordination and act as a 'single point of truth' for all aspects of communication between the promoter and the various organisations or groups of people who will be employed by the promoter to execute the project. While others will input into the process and converse directly with the promoter at various times, it is essential that the project manager has full knowledge of such actions and is in overall control of the project. This is a key lesson that may be seen from many projects. The project manager should establish definitions of roles, authority, communication and reporting that bind everyone to the objectives of the project.

The project manager will develop a range of documents, tools, techniques and metrics to deliver the project. This will typically include:

- stakeholder management
- project initiation document
- project execution plan
- master programmes and schedules, using work breakdown structures or similar methods
- design responsibility matrix
- risk registers
- project controls and earned value analysis (EVA) reports.

Project team

The project team should be formed with the requisite expertise and resources to assist the project manager in planning, executing and managing all the remaining stages of the project through to practical completion and handover.

If a design and build or early contractor involvement (ECI) route has been selected, then the contractor can be employed within the team from this stage.

Whether within the promoter's own organisation, working for consultants or others advising the promoter, or within the contractor's organisation, the team should include staff that have recent experience of the construction, operation and maintenance of similar projects. Team knowledge of historical issues, for example recurring problems with materials or processes, allows learning to be imported and generates a principle of continuous improvement, which in turn provides the opportunity for successive projects to be more efficiently designed and managed.

The structure of the team should vary for each stage of the work, and will depend upon the size and complexity of the project and how much it can draw upon the resources of established departments within the promoter's organisation, consultants and others (Wearne, 1989).

Flexibility is also required to accommodate sometimes significant and rapid change in the size and composition of the team. Work activities can be undertaken in sequence, where development of one aspect is dependent on the output from earlier work, or in parallel, where this is not the case.

In general terms, parallel development will give rise to programme time-savings, but imports some risk of integration of the various project elements. Effective risk management overcomes this risk as the project progresses.

Project controls

Effective project control is key to aligning programme and schedule with the measures of time, cost, quality and health and safety. In recent times, project controls have become a sub-division of many project management organisations, emphasising its role in the successful delivery of projects.

Most project control systems for major projects now utilise sophisticated software solutions, often bespoke to a particular organisation and capable of providing a 'dashboard' of information covering cost management, change management and control, risk management and document control.

The project manager should establish procedures for:

- work breakdown, definition of authority, responsibilities and control of changes
- planning and progress monitoring of office and site manpower needs, project design and services, preparation and placing of contracts and other procurement, construction, critical sub-contracts, testing, commissioning and handover
- health and safety plans, statutory approvals, audits and reporting
- change management and the introduction of variations
- risk management
- cost estimating, cost management and trend analysis
- equipment and material ordering, inspection and delivery
- quality management plans
- audit traceability
- mapping and benchmarking of performance
- 'lessons learned' and knowledge transfer capture and dissemination
- earned value reconciliation
- project management information
- reporting to the promoter
- document records and control.

Planning

The purpose of planning the work for a project is to think ahead about what is needed to achieve the objectives of the project. Programmes and reports should include the amount of detail needed by their intended users. Too little information can leave the team uncertain about what is wanted and what is happening. Too much can be counterproductive, as people will ignore it or at best only look for what they assume matters to them.

The planning of a project must allow time for the legal requirements to obtain approval of design and construction by statutory authorities and for tendering procedures governed by EU procurement rules. Planning techniques should be used which are appropriate to the scale, urgency and risks of the project (see the publications on project planning and control listed in Appendix B). As a minimum, it is recommended that key milestones, trigger points and constraints are clearly identified and monitored.

With the advent of sophisticated programming and planning software, many complex projects now include specific stipulations for the use of these programs. Power project, MS Project and Primavera are among the software products currently in common use.

Monitoring and reporting

All but minor routine projects need a system for monitoring progress and costs from the start of design to provide a basis for regular reviews of achievement and trends compared to programme and budget. The scope of the data that are to be presented in a report should be agreed with the users.

Attention to cost trends and probable outcomes is important on most projects, the exception being urgent work. For all projects, speed in reporting costs is usually more valuable than accuracy, to enable action to be taken on trends. Quick data should be followed by accurate data and analysis of the causes of savings and extra costs in order to correct first impressions and improve the information available for estimating the costs of future projects.

Most monitoring now includes use of schedule performance indicators (SPIs) and cost performance indicators (CPIs) to allow data to be readily assimilated and trends identified.

Risk analysis and management

Project risks

The information used to decide whether to proceed with a project is inevitably based upon forecasts, predictions and assumptions about the future conditions and costs that may affect its design, construction and commissioning, and often its operation and sometimes also its eventual decommissioning, demolition and site restoration. Political events, weather, the quality of design, unknown ground conditions, bankruptcies/insolvencies, plant/equipment failures, industrial relations, accidents, mistakes and criminal actions are all risks which may affect the progress, cost or economic value of proceeding. The identification and assessment of risks is an ongoing activity throughout the project life cycle.

Not every party to a project will have the same view of a risk and how it should be managed. The project manager should therefore establish the promoter's policy on risks and inform all the project team.

To assist this process, a comprehensive risk register should be developed, managed and maintained throughout the life of the project. Various software packages are available which provide tools for calculating/assessing the probability of events occurring and the likely consequence on cost and compiling a consolidated risk profile. In common use are @Risk and Active Risk Manager, although most simple spreadsheet applications are capable of coping with statistical methods and simulation to provide guidance on risk management decision-making.

The common assumption in modern forms of contract and procurement is that risks should be 'owned' by the party or parties best equipped to bear the risk, but due to varying perceptions of the concept of risk, some promoters prefer and pursue a policy of perceived 'total risk transfer'. However, analysis of such procurement routes by the National Audit Office and others shows that this latter attitude is unlikely to provide the most cost-effective outcome for the promoter.

Risk management
Numerous models and frameworks to guide the implementation of risk management in civil engineering projects exist. ISO 31000 (ISO, 2009) sets out some generic guidance and *RAMP* (see Appendix B) provides a civil engineering specific approach. Most frameworks share a common sequential process, shown in the Figure 4.1.

Risk identification
Research, experience and checklists can be used to identify the sources of possible risks to the project, including physical, environmental, societal, commercial, political, legal, financial, operational, technical, resourcing and logistical risks. Risk workshops are

Figure 4.1 The risk management process

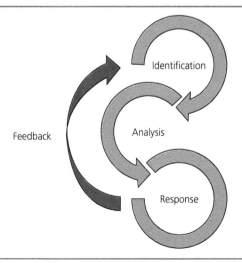

useful forums for developing the initial risk register and should draw on a 'broad church' of stakeholders to ensure that the intended beneficiaries and those negatively affected by the project are represented in the risk register.

Risk analysis
The probability and potential effects of each risk are assessed, using, among other methods, the product of likelihood and consequence. Risks are ordinarily rated on a simple integer scale of 1–5 where 1 = insignificant/very low likelihood/consequence and 5 = very high likelihood/consequence. Other methods may also be used, such as sensitivity analysis, decision trees, probabilistic analysis and simulation. For risk analysis to remain effective regular risk reviews should be undertaken and the outcomes of that process disseminated accordingly.

Risk response
For each risk, decisions are made as to whether to

- take no action, if it is too unlikely or its potential effects are likely to be trivial
- eliminate it, by modifying some aspects of the project or revising the proposed project scope
- transfer it, usually to an insurer or a construction contractor, or
- bear it, allow for its possible cost and other effects and manage it.

Risk feedback
The impact of the decisions taken at the risk response stage should be reviewed. The 'lessons learned' or 'after-action review' process is the usual mechanism.

Health, safety and welfare management
Attention to and observance of health and safety legislation is a professional and legal duty placed on each and every person involved with the promotion, design, construction and subsequent operation of a civil engineering project. The nature of civil engineering is such that projects are potentially lethal working environments if there are not adequate planning, management and supervision safeguards. There are a number of characteristics of civil engineering projects that potentially give rise to health, safety and welfare issues, including:

- varying degrees of uncertainty
- innovative and novel working methods
- unexpected geotechnical issues
- impact of weather and the outdoor environment
- multi-organisation interfaces with complex channels of communication
- complex operations and plant/equipment
- foreign workforces with limited local language skills.

There has been a substantial reduction in the number of fatal injuries in construction in the last 40 years. Nevertheless, the construction industry accounts for a significant proportion of all workplace-related fatalities and injuries in the UK. The most recent statistics available from the Health and Safety Executive (HSE) (for the reporting year 2013/14) indicate the following

- There were 42 fatal injuries to construction workers, 14 of these fatalities were to the self-employed. This compares with an average of 46 over the previous 5 years – including an average of 17 to the self-employed.
- There were an estimated 76 000 total cases of work-related ill health, of which 31 000 were new cases.
- An estimated 2.3 million working days were lost in 2013/14, 1.7 million due to ill health and 592 000 due to workplace injury, making a total of 1.1 days lost per worker.
- Injuries and new cases of ill health resulting largely from current working conditions in workers in construction cost society over £1.1 billion a year.

Legislation

The most important piece of UK legislation is the Health and Safety at Work etc. Act 1974. The Act sets out responsibilities of employers and employees, based on the premise that individuals/organisations should 'ensure so far as is reasonably practicable the health, safety and welfare at work of all their employees'. The key phrase here is 'reasonably practicable' and this has been the subject of legal debate over many decades. The definition of 'reasonably practicable' was set out by the Court of Appeal (in its judgment of *Edwards* v. *National Coal Board* [1949]):

> 'Reasonably practicable' is a narrower term than 'physically possible' ... a computation must be made by the owner in which the quantum of risk is placed on one scale and the sacrifice involved in the measures necessary for averting the risk (whether in money, time or trouble) is placed in the other, and that, if it be shown that there is a gross disproportion between them – the risk being insignificant in relation to the sacrifice – the defendants discharge the onus on them.

In reality, it is the responsibly of the courts to determine what 'reasonably practicable' is and this invariably depends upon the context of the case. While the Health and Safety at Work Act etc. 1974 is a commonly used legislative instrument in the prosecution of health and safety offences, the legislation suffers from a weakness. In traditional UK law, the body corporate is distinct in law from the individuals who comprise the corporation. This has, historically, presented problems in the case of fatalities; the prosecution of common law manslaughter ('corporate manslaughter') was difficult to apply to a charge of common law manslaughter against companies (corporate manslaughter) was difficult to undertake as charges still had to be brought against an individual known as the 'controlling mind' (the identification principle). This problem was addressed in the Corporate Manslaughter and Corporate Homicide Act 2007.

Case study 1: The 'test' case for the Corporate Manslaughter and Corporate Homicide Act 2007

The case of R v. Cotswold Geotechnical (Holdings) Ltd (2008) resulted in the first criminal conviction under the Corporate Manslaughter and Corporate Homicide Act 2007 (CMCH07). Alexander Wright, a 27-year-old graduate geologist, died in 2008 when a trench in which he was working collapsed. It was found that the company's method of undertaking 'trial pits' was dangerous and at variance with standard industry guidelines. Cotswold Geotechnical (Holdings) Ltd was found guilty under the 2007 Act and received a fine of £385 000. The Act is concerned with corporate liability and does not apply to directors or other individuals who have a senior role in the company or organisation. It should be noted that existing health and safety offences and gross negligence manslaughter continue to apply to individuals where appropriate and in this case a director was charged with gross negligence manslaughter (the charge was stayed due to ill health of the defendant). While the number of convictions under the Act is increasing, there remains a degree of scepticism surrounding its efficacy. The three subsequent prosecutions, R v. J Murray and Sons Ltd (2013), R v. JMW Farms Ltd (2012) and R v. Lion Steel Ltd (2012), suggest that prosecutions tend to be of small, owner-managed companies and convictions by guilty plea seem likely to continue if the alternative is the risk to one of the owners of personal conviction and imprisonment. The most recent case, R v. Peter Mawson Ltd (2015), involved the death of a maintenance worker at height, resulting in a fine of £200 000 for the company and a personal conviction under Health and Safety at Work etc. Act 1974 (HSAW74) for the owner, who was given a suspended prison sentence and a community service order.

The HSE position on the responsibility of the board (of an organisation) to set appropriate strategy with good health, safety and welfare in mind is well explained in the guidance notes that accompany CMCH07 legislation and HSAW74. The key principles of that guidance are as follows:

- Strong and active leadership from the top
  - visible, active commitment from the board
  - establishing effective 'downwards' communication systems and management structures
  - integration of good health and safety management with business decisions.

- Worker involvement
  - engaging the workforce in the promotion and achievement of safe and healthy conditions
  - effective 'upwards' communication
  - providing high-quality training.
- Assessment and review
  - identifying and managing health and safety risks
  - accessing (and following) competent advice
  - monitoring, reporting and reviewing performance.

Generally speaking, good health and safety management offers other significant business benefits, including reduced costs and reduced risks (employee absence and turnover rates are lower, accidents are fewer, the threat of legal action is lessened; improved standing among suppliers and partners; a better reputation for corporate responsibility among investors, customers and communities; and increased productivity) and employees are healthier, happier and better motivated.

The specific law related to the design, construction, maintenance and decommissioning of civil infrastructure projects is variously described in the:

- Construction (Design and Management) Regulations (CDM) 2015
- Control of Substances Hazardous to Health Regulations (COSHH) 2002
- Health and Safety (Consultation with Employees) Regulations 1996
- Lifting Operations and Lifting Equipment Regulations (LOLER) 1998
- Management of Health and Safety at Work Regulations 1999
- Provision and Use of Work Equipment Regulations (PUWER) 1998
- Notification of Conventional Tower Cranes Regulations 2010
- Work at Height Regulations 2005.

In Chapter 5 we will take a closer look at the CDM Regulations 2015, a piece of legislation that first came into force on 31 March 1995 as the Construction (Design and Management) Regulations 1994. The regulations were essentially the implementation of EU Directive 92/57/EEC on the implementation of minimum safety and health requirements at temporary or mobile construction sites. The regulations placed legal duties on those that promoted and designed civil engineering works as well as on those organisations responsible for construction.

Quality management
Quality management is the process of ensuring that the project meets the promoter's requirements for economic and safe quality of design, materials and construction (Baden Hellard, 1993). Many promoters will only employ consultants and contractors

who meet national and international standards for quality assurance and technical competence; this is often known as 'pre-qualification'. In the UK, a number of schemes are in existence to aid promoters in the selection of consultants and contractors. Aside from registration with the chartered institutions, Constructionline, Safecontractor and ContractorPlus can be used to guide appointments. Training, quality assurance systems and detailed supervision on site help greatly to achieve increased productivity and high standards of quality.

Quality assurance (QA) procedures are a systematic way of specifying actions which will give confidence that quality requirements will be achieved. These procedures should

- state how the quality standards required for a project are to be decided and communicated
- establish how and how far proposed methods of work are to be assessed and improved to achieve adequate standards of work
- specify how the records of standards achieved are to be compiled, coded and recorded
- include auditing of the effectiveness of the procedures.

QA procedures should be clear and brief, their purpose being to anticipate problems. QA should be required for a project only if the cost of establishing and applying it is expected to be less than the total cost risks if there were no QA system. Quality management policies and QA systems should therefore be reviewed regularly to see if they are cost-effective.

Promoter's procurement strategy
Procurement strategies
It is important that procurement delivers a successful outcome for the promoter and their stakeholders. It should not be concerned simply with achieving lowest capital cost; considerations such as whole-life cost, sustainability, health and safety, and corporate social responsibility are also important. Other considerations include:

- transparency and fairness in supply chains
- long-term strategic alliances with suppliers to enhance business sustainability
- using contracts which are appropriate to the project.

There are a number of different strategies available to deliver civil engineering/building projects. These have evolved over time to reflect changes in the structure of the construction industry and changes in promoters' requirements, their priorities and external influences, such as the financial and political environment, availability of funding, sources of finance, legislative changes and so on.

A project procurement strategy is the output of the process of deciding how best to deliver the project. It will marry the business case, programme and project objectives and required deliverables (including considerations of time, cost and quality) with available sources of finance and reflect the promoter's approach to risk.

The procurement strategy exerts considerable influence over the project team's ability to achieve a successful balance between the costs, time and quality parameters.

Procurement strategies reflect fundamental differences in the allocation of risk and responsibilities between the parties. Additionally, the suitability of the different approaches has to be considered in relation to the specific nature of the individual project, as there is no one procurement route suitable for all. In developing the optimum procurement route, the promoter's core business and strategic objectives and constraints must be considered, evaluated and prioritised.

Strategy choices

Business objectives and corporate policy drivers need to be considered in addition to the normal project drivers.

An optimum procurement strategy will evolve as a consequence of working through a staged evaluation process, which may include consideration of some or all of the following:

1   Should the promoter employ consultants and contractors, or carry out all or some of the work with its own employees?
2   To what extent do the business drivers, project objectives and sources of finance influence the structure of the delivery team?
3   What is the envisaged shape of the project delivery team? If more than one organisation, are they to be employed sequentially or together?
4   Are enabling works desirable or necessary?
5   What are the legal considerations – planning, EU compliance, land acquisition or rights and implementation powers?
6   Who is to be responsible for what? Who is to be responsible for defining objectives and priorities, design, quality, operating and maintenance decisions, health and safety studies, approvals, scheduling, procurement, construction, equipment installation, inspection, testing, commissioning and for managing each of these?
7   How will the intended operation and maintenance of the finished project, and perhaps also its eventual decommissioning, demolition and site restoration, be related to the process of design and construction and to the parties engaged in procuring the project?

8 Who is to bear the risks of defining the project, investing in it, obtaining the necessary approvals, specifying performance, design risks, ground conditions, selecting sub-contractors, site productivity, mistakes and accidents?

9 What terms of payment will motivate all parties to achieve the promoter's objectives – including payment for design, equipment, construction and services?

10 Is a form of incentive mechanism appropriate? If so, should it be time, cost or quality orientated – or a combination of each?

Some of the answers may be dictated by law, government policy or by financing bodies.

Contract strategy

The major contracting strategies are described below, which includes a commentary of the core functions and responsibilities undertaken by the project manager, common terminology and descriptions of the various contracting routes and contractual relationships and interaction.

The project manager

In Chapter 2, the term 'project manager' has been adopted to convey the role of the promoter's lead adviser. In the various contracting routes that are available under a procurement strategy, the role will require varying skill sets and the functions of the project manager will vary accordingly.

Traditionally in civil engineering in the UK, the consulting engineer was the adviser to the promoter from the inception of the project, as described in Chapter 2, and the route chosen was almost exclusively traditional contracting.

Under this route, when the project was sanctioned, a consulting engineer was appointed to be responsible for design, preparation of the construction contract and tender assessment. This role was then generally extended to the construction phase, where the consulting engineer became *the engineer* named in the construction contract with powers and duties to supervise *the works* and make decisions on design, construction and payment. The role of the engineer was/is often delegated to a site-based 'resident engineer', who acts as the engineer's representative and may be assisted in the maintenance of quality and inspection of progress by a 'clerk of works'.

More recently, as it has become clear that 'one size fits all' is not a maxim that is appropriate to all civil engineering projects, alternative forms of contracting have been used. This has particularly been a consequence of the Latham Principles, colloquially known as 'Constructing the Team', and Egan's 'Re-thinking Construction', from the 1990s.

In some contracting routes and forms of contract the title 'the project manager' is now used to mean the role of supervising the works. Other titles, including 'the architect',

Figure 4.2 Traditional procurement strategy arrangement

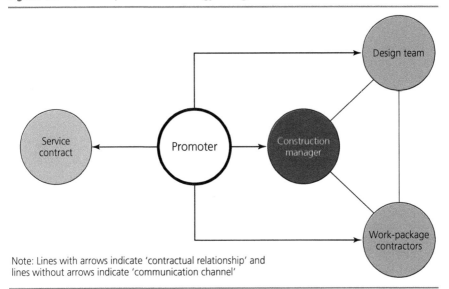

Note: Lines with arrows indicate 'contractual relationship' and lines without arrows indicate 'communication channel'

'the supervising officer' and 'the contractor administrator', are also used for similar roles in large building and some civil engineering contracts. The person's powers and duties vary from contract to contract, but in principle operate as indicated in Figure 4.2.

However, the role of the engineer with powers and duties to supervise the works is still prevalent in international civil engineering contracts.

Contracts for construction work

It is usual to invite contractors to compete for a contract for construction work, in the expectation that they will plan to do the work efficiently and therefore at minimum cost. Unless the project is procured under an existing framework arrangement, EU tendering rules (in the case of public projects) are likely to apply (see Table 4.1). EU requirements only apply to contacts above a certain value. The EU Procurement Regulations provide details of the required process and guidance in the application. It should be noted that EU rules do not apply to projects funded entirely by the private sector initiatives, although it will often be the case that frameworks exist within specific promoter bodies, or that a process akin to that in the public sector is desirable. It is usual to go through an expression of interest procedure and to then refine the tender invitation list by means of a transparent pre-qualification process.

Table 4.1 Public Contract Regulations

Public Contract Regulations	EU threshold applicable from 1 January 2014	UK threshold applicable from 1 January 2014
Supply and service contracts/design contests awarded by central government bodies subject to the WTO GPA	€134 000	£111 676
Supply and service contracts/design contests awarded by other contracting authorities	€207 000	£172 514
Works contracts, subsidised works contracts and works concession contracts	€5 186 000	£4 322 012

Key: WTO GPA = World Trade Organization Agreement on Government Procurement (a plurilateral agreement within the framework of the WTO)

In 2014, new EU procurement directives emerged in addition to the existing Directive 2009/81/EU (Defence and Security) (Table 4.2):

- Public Sector: Directive 2014/24/EU of the European Parliament and of the Council of 26 February 2014 on public procurement and repealing Directive 2004/18/EC
- Concessions: Directive 2014/23/EU of the European Parliament and of the Council of 26 February 2014 on the award of concession contracts
- Utilities: Directive 2014/25/EU of the European Parliament and of the Council of 26 February 2014 on procurement by entities operating in the water, energy, transport and postal services sectors and repealing Directive 2004/17/EC (see Table 4.3).

So far, only a part of these changes have been promulgated into UK law. The UK government prioritised the Public Sector Directive in an attempt to accelerate deregulation and improve the simplicity of rules for where most procurement spend and activity takes place. The UK's implementing regulations, the Public Contracts Regulations 2015, were laid before Parliament on 5 February 2015 and came into force on 26 February

Table 4.2 Defence and Security Public Contracts Regulations

Defence and Security Public Contracts Regulations	EU threshold applicable from 1 January 2014	UK threshold applicable from 1 January 2014
Supply and service contracts	€414 000	£345 028
Works contracts	€5 186 000	£4 322 012

Table 4.3 Utilities Contract Regulations

Utilities Contract Regulations	EU threshold applicable from 1 January 2014	UK threshold applicable from 1 January 2014
Supply and service contracts/ design contests	€414 000	£345 028
Works contracts	€5 186 000	£4 322 012

2015. The changes include some relaxation of the previous restrictions on how contracts are let and of the financial limits at which various requirements apply.

Selected contractors are invited to tender on an equal basis, competing on technical proposals, price and evidence of past performance. Competing on price and speed of starting work is common practice for sub-contracts. It is usual for the contractor who has submitted the most economically advantageous tender against the award criteria to be appointed. It is worth noting that unless this is clearly the case, or the promoter has well evidenced reasons to do otherwise, the award of the contract may be subject to legal challenge, as may also occur if the EU requirements have not been followed with sufficient transparency.

Most contracts are for the construction of a defined asset (i.e. a road, bridge or building) although exceptions are term/maintenance contracts, those under a private finance initiative (PFI) or public private partnership (PPP) or a private sector client equivalent involving some kind of facilities contract and/or lease-back arrangements. In the commentary below, we cover the following contractual options:

1   Traditional.
2   Design and build.
3   Develop and construct.
4   Construction management/management contracting.
5   Term service and maintenance contracts.
6   PPPs.

1. Traditional contracts

The tradition form of procurement remains a commonly used approach for construction projects in the UK. Lump-sum contracts are perhaps the most popular, although modern forms of contract have emphasised the benefits of integration between the design and construction team at earlier stages in the project life cycle.

■   'Lump-sum' – a single 'all-in' price for all of the works is agreed before the works begin on site. This is also known as the 'contract sum'.

- Measurement/remeasurement – the contract sum cannot be determined on execution of the contract and is therefore calculated on completion of the works, based on 'remeasurement' of the actual work carried out and the rates tendered.
- Cost-reimbursement – the contractor is reimbursed for the actual cost of the works and receives an additional fee over and above this. It is often known as 'cost plus'.

Traditional lump-sum arrangements can be through a single- or two-stage tender process. Single-stage tendering will incorporate a full design prior to tendering for the construction works. With two-stage tendering, a contractor is brought on board early, tendering against an outline design and programme. The design is then completed with the contractor's specialist input and second-stage tendering is carried out on the basis of fully designed work packages. Two-stage tendering is sometimes selected over single-stage when the works are complex, design team involvement is required during contractor tendering, and/or ECI is desirable.

Cost implication

Lump-sum contracting can provide a high degree of cost certainty, providing that full design is achieved prior to tendering. Without the latter, the promoter is exposed to potential claims. Two-stage tendering has become popular among some promoters, who believe that it can provide a more 'robust' lump-sum price on the basis that the contractor is involved earlier in the process and interfaces with the design team prior to finalising the price. It is important to note that a 'lump-sum price' is not a 'fixed price' and that it will not be the final price. There are a number of events that can occur whereby the lump sum is varied; these typically include:

- delay/disruption
- force majeure/acts of God
- provisional sums
- inflationary risk
- variations
- claims and disputes.

Quality implication

As design is retained by the promoter's appointed designers, the desired level of quality should be maintained consistently throughout. There is however a limitation for designers to communicate directly with specialist suppliers and to effectively involve them at an early point in the project design process, which can be mitigated to some degree if the two-stage tendering process is used. In addition, novated specialist suppliers or sub-contractors can partly address this issue.

Programme implication

In order to obtain full design prior to tendering, lump-sum contracting requires a significant lead-in as only limited overlap occurs between design and construction. ECI can be achieved through a two-stage process.

Flexibility implication

While change can be incorporated under this route the tendency is for contractors to attempt to maximise rather than mitigate its effect. The contractor's ability to do this is heightened by the fact that the promoter and their advisers have no contractual relationship with the contractor's sub-contractors during the contract works.

2. Design and build

Under a design and build route, the contractor is engaged earlier in the project life cycle and will initially tender against 'outline' scheme requirements, for example a performance specification and drawings and draft contract (often these documents are colloquially known as 'employer's (promoter's) requirements'). Design and build contracts are known by various other terms, including 'design and construct', 'package deal', 'all-in' and 'turnkey'.

Once initially tendered, the design is worked up to a benchmark level (often against pre-determined criteria) where the contractor and promoter feel they are able to enter into contract. The contractor may engage their own design team in this process or provision can be made for the promoter's team involved in the initial, pre-tender, phase to be 'novated'; that is, have their design contract transferred from being with the promoter to being with the main contractor. See Figure 4.3.

Cost implication

As with traditional lump-sum contracting, design and build provides single point responsibility and a greater degree of cost certainty, providing the promoter's requirements are fully defined. Undefined promoter's requirements will open the risk of a subsequent claim. However, it is important to consider at what stage and under what terms the 'price' is 'fixed'. Arguably, if a design and build contract is for a 'fixed out-turn price' and the contract is agreed before the detailed design is completed, then greater cost certainty can be achieved than with a 'traditional contract', but there will be less certainty in terms of what the promoter will actually get for his or her money. From this perspective, risk needs to be fully considered and appropriately placed.

Quality implication

As the design responsibility is transferred to the contractor's team, the promoter loses direct control and hence quality could arguably be compromised. While effective documentation can mitigate this to some extent, the contractor's focus may lie in commercial issues rather than design. Options exist to either novate the design team to the

Figure 4.3 Design and build (ECI) procurement strategy arrangement

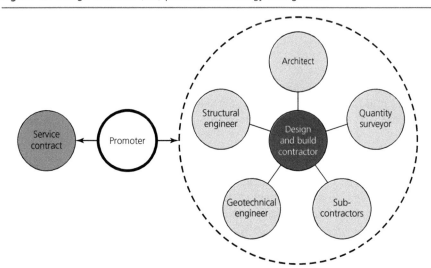

contractor or to largely complete the design prior to handing over to the contractor to mitigate these concerns. There is a 'middle way' in which the design team (or some portion of it) are engaged by the main contractor to complete the detailed design, while they (or some part of the original design team) are also retained by the promoter/client to oversee the design and construction and to certify quality and approve stage payments for partial completion and so on. If the latter option is chosen, it has to be recognised that some benefit of the contractor's design input and commercial advantage is lost.

Programme implication
Design and build can achieve a faster start on site due to the overlapping of design and construction and through ECI. However, the programme must reflect sufficient time for definition of the promoter's requirements. Procurement can be on a single- or two-stage basis, with the latter providing overall programme savings.

Flexibility implication
Design and build does not readily accommodate change in the promoter's requirements. The contractor, through their control of both design and sub-contractors, has a strong negotiating position and may look to maximise this effect for their financial gain.

3. Develop and construct
Develop and construct may be viewed as a derivative (or 'son of') design and build, but it recognises that most of the design work has already been completed. It therefore obviates

some of the drawbacks with design and build, but reduces the contractor's ability to bring their skills and knowledge to the design phase. As with design and build, design responsibility will be passed to the contractor as well as the construction risk.

4. Management/package route – construction management/management contracting

The management/package route is usually considered under two main strategies: construction management (CM) and management contracting (MC). Both effectively use a series of specialist trade contractors to carry out the construction works, the difference arises in the contractual relationships.

Under CM, a construction manager is appointed to be the contractor, albeit that their role is limited to provision of site facilities and management and coordination of the construction works packages. The construction manager and the trade contractors are all appointed by the promoter. In MC, it is the management contractor who engages the trade contractors; control and responsibility for the supply chain is therefore passed to the management contractor.

Under the MC strategy the managing organisation is effectively employed as an extension to the promoter's own organisation. Duties vary from project to project, for instance in the responsibilities for coordinating design and construction. The duties and powers of the managing organisation need to be stated consistently in its contract with the promoter and in the contracts of the trade contractors.

In either case, payment to the construction manager or management contractor is by way of a fee, either cost plus or lump sum for the provision of site facilities. This fee may be set in a variety of ways, for example based on a 'scheduled rates and time', 'audited cost-plus' or 'percentage of construction costs' basis.

The promoter should possess a very good understanding of construction practices before embarking on this route. See Figure 4.4.

Cost implication

A CM/MC procurement route overlaps design and construction, with the work being packaged and tenders achieved progressively as design packages are completed. As such, the promoter does not have the benefit of a lump-sum price prior to commitment (unless the route is adapted to accommodate this) and is thus exposed to financial risk. Mitigation is available through knowledgeable cost management, pre-market testing and early tendering of significant work packages. With CM, the promoter is in direct contract with the supply chain, so they are better able to control cost risk than with MC but potentially more directly liable for the knock-on implications of sub-contractor default.

Figure 4.4 Construction management procurement strategy

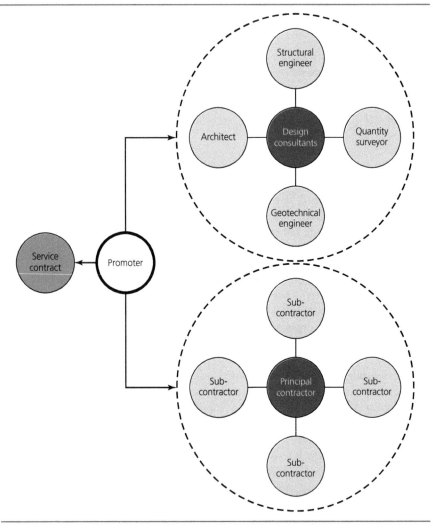

Quality implication

Quality is maintained as the promoter retains control of the design team. Flexibility is also inherent because various work packages can be let as 'design and construct'. In addition, the promoter has the added advantage of a professional construction manager who is independent by virtue of having no financial interest beyond their management role, although this does rather depend on the basis of the construction manager's fees, the possible 'ownership structure' of the construction manager and of other contractors' suppliers, and on an absence of corrupt payments or influence.

Programme implication

The CM/MC routes provide major advantages in terms of programme as design and construction are overlapped. The construction manager/management contractor also has the ability to re-plan and to incentivise trade contractors, particularly in order to mitigate delay or accommodate change, but the promoter will carry the associated time and cost risks of disruption beyond the initial delay cause, whether of their making or not. The construction manager/management contractor is appointed prior to completion of full design to assist in programming, cost planning, constructability issues and to procure the works.

Flexibility implication

CM by its nature provides inherent flexibility in terms of managing and incorporating change. Due to the independence of the construction manager, the true consequences of change can be ascertained and re-planning of the works can be totally transparent. Direct access to trade contractors facilitates this process. MC is less flexible, although change can be incorporated more readily later in the process than with the traditional route on the basis that design and construction overlap.

5. Term service/maintenance contracts

These types of contracts are used when a promoter has a need for an ongoing sequence of works, but where the extent is unclear. They may therefore be looked on as a contract for a series of contracts (term) or for dealing with planned and unplanned repairs and renewals (maintenance). They may equally be seen as framework arrangements, where mini competitive tenders can be sought for specific works where a series of contractors already have an umbrella contract for term and maintenance works. They are usually let for fixed periods of time, often 3–5 years, to provide opportunity for contractors to build efficient working practices, while giving the promoter the opportunity to ensure pricing remains competitive over reasonable periods of time. Contracts may be tendered against schedules of rates for various works or lump sum pricing/fee percentages.

6. Public private partnerships

A PPP is the generic term to describe collaboration and joint working between the public and private sectors through contract or through a joint venture, to deliver infrastructure assets and services. In the UK, the most common form of PPP was the PFI, although its use has declined somewhat in recent years.

The PFI was introduced in 1992 by the then Conservative government in a decision taken by the Chancellor of the Exchequer, Norman Lamont, to encourage private investment in major public building/engineering projects. A number of motivations, including a desire to achieve reductions in the public sector borrowing requirement and to improve the transfer of risk to the private sector, were catalysts to the growth of PFI as a procurement route in the UK.

Under PFI, the normal arrangement is for the finance of the design and construction phase to be provided by the private sector and for its costs plus some profit to be recovered over an operational period of typically 20–30 years, termed a 'concession'. During this period, the concessionaire receives an income stream, which may be: from selling some output of the project, such as electricity generated by a power station; directly from users, for instance from drivers using a toll road; in the form of a facilities fee paid by a public sector body, which may be related to the usage of the project or to some time or quality related metric of service availability; or from some combination of such sources.

A variety of concession arrangements have been developed, with various names, but not all of these are appropriately regarded as forms of PFI arrangements. These include:

- Build, operate, transfer (BOT) and build, own, operate, transfer (BOOT) – a private entity contracts with a private or public sector body to finance, design, construct, and operate an asset over a concession period. The difference between BOT and BOOT lies in whether the promoter or the concessionaire has ownership of the asset during the concession period.
- Design, build, finance, transfer (DBFT) – involves private sector capital finance but not necessarily private sector operation.
- Design, build, finance, operate (DBFO) – very similar to BOOT except that there is no ownership transfer.
- Design, build, operate, transfer (DBOT) – may not necessarily involve much (if any) private sector capital finance.
- Design, build, operate, maintain (DBOM) – involves both operation and maintenance, but not necessarily finance and not ownership of the asset (e.g. the original Manchester Metrolink light-rail scheme was a DBOM project).
- Design, build, finance, maintain (DBFM) – involves both finance and maintenance, but not operation (the infrastructure for the London Docklands Light Railway extension to Lewisham was originally procured as a DBFM project).
- Design, construct, manage, finance (DCMF) – popular in the procurement of hospital and prison buildings in the UK. One of the first PFI schemes in the UK, HM Prison Altcourse near Liverpool (see Case Study 3), adopted a DCMF arrangement.

The term 'PFI' is strictly a particular form of PPP that was devised by the UK Treasury and also adopted in Australia whereby facilities (or services) required by a public sector body could be procured without recourse (or with much reduced recourse) to public sector finance. PFI typically achieves the provision of capital assets for use in the delivery

Figure 4.5 SPC structure of a PPP procurement strategy

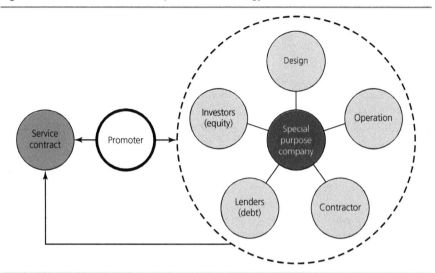

of a service normally provided by the public sector without substantial direct increases in the public sector debt. The contractual arrangements are complex, requiring a contracting authority, concession agreement, performance specification and contracts between the special purpose company (SPC) and its key supply chain, many of whom may well also be stakeholders in the SPC. See Figure 4.5.

Case study 2: The Skye Bridge Crossing, Scotland's first PFI scheme

The Skye Bridge Crossing was opened in October 1995 and provided the first physical infrastructure connection between the west coast of mainland Scotland and the Isle of Skye. Built under a DBFO agreement, it was Scotland's first infrastructure PFI deal, providing a replacement to the ageing ferry service. The PFI contract was awarded to Miller–Dywidag, an SPC composed of Miller Construction and DYWIDAG Systems International (a German engineering company) with project finance provided by the Bank of America. The complex, 500 m long single-span prestressed concrete arch, supported by two piers, was designed in collaboration with Arup. Despite receiving widespread acclaim for the engineering challenges that the project team had overcome, in particular the inhospitable climate and the construction of the caissons, the bridge became embroiled in a political argument concerning the acceptability of the tolls that the SPC charged.

Case study 3: HM Prison Altcourse

In 1995, the UK government (through the Home Office) let a 25 year DBFO PFI contract for a new Category A and B high-security prison to Fazakerley Prison Services Limited (FPSL). The SPC was formed by Group 4 Securitas and Tarmac Construction Limited, to design, construct and finance the new 600 prisoner-place establishment located in the Fazakerley district of Liverpool, near Aintree race-course. The design and construction of the prison involved a high degree of standardisation of components and modular assembly, designed to achieve greater cost and schedule certainty. This resulted in handover of the prison some 5 months ahead of schedule. In 1999, the SPC refinanced the project, which improved the expected returns to shareholders creating additional benefits of £10.7 million in total, over the duration of the contract. In a subsequent evidence session by the Public Accounts Committee, MPs heard that 'had the whole of this amount been made available to FPSL's shareholders, their returns from the project, which had been estimated at £17.5 million at the time the contract was awarded, would have increased by 61%' and that 'the projected internal rate of return to FPSL's share-holders increased from 16% to 39%'.

PPPs will be procured against the ultimate (initiating) promoter's requirements, using performance specifications and requirements for the legal, contractual, financial and commercial model. Once a preferred bidder is selected, negotiations take place to seal the contract, termed financial close. As a result of the complexities involved in the PPP procurement process, it can often take a period of several years from the start of procure-ment and inviting potential bidders to achieve financial close and it can involve significant resource cost to construct a bid.

Contracts for consultancy services

Traditionally, consulting engineers in the UK and internationally were employed by promoters under standard terms of engagement and fixed scales of fees stage-by-stage through a project. Other consultancy work for promoters or contractors was most often reimbursed at cost plus a fixed fee. Consultants are now increasingly invited to compete by price to provide design or other services, whether employed by promoters or contrac-tors or as part of a joint venture/SPC for PFI/PPP arrangements.

Contract responsibilities

Responsibilities and duties of the promoter

The promoter's objectives, responsibilities, duties and liabilities should normally be stated in all contracts with consultants and contractors, including:

- defining the functions that the project is to perform

- providing information and data held by them and required by the other parties
- obtaining the necessary legal authority to allow construction of the project
- acquiring ownership or rights to use the necessary land
- making payment.

The promoter may of course arrange for some or all of these duties to be performed on their behalf by a consultant or a contractor.

Responsibilities and duties of the contractor
Contractor's responsibilities vary depending on the nature of the procurement route selected.

In traditional and design and build routes, contractors usually selected are those who, on account of their resources and experience, are able to undertake responsibility as main contractor for the construction of the whole of a project, although they may *sub-let* parts of the work to specialist or other sub-contractors. This is a simplification, of course; on a large project (e.g. Crossrail) the project may be sub-divided into a large number of separate main contracts.

Specialist contractors
In MC and CM, contractors selected for the primary role by the promoter may either be firms of main contractors with specialist divisions or firms who have sought to build their business around MC and CM routes. The supply chain below the management contractor or construction manager is then usually drawn from contractors who confine their activities to selected classes of work and are referred to as specialist or *trades contractors*. This specialisation enables them to employ skilled staff and plant particularly suited to their work, but without carrying the same overhead requirements associated with main contractors. In some cases their designs and techniques are protected by patents, exclusive licenses or other legal restrictions.

Alternative contract management arrangements
International practice
International practice varies significantly across the various global regions, and for the purposes of this guide, it is difficult to give more than a flavour of the regional approaches.

In the eastward extension of the EU, because of an historical tendency to use the public sector to both design and construct projects, the financial infrastructure lends itself to a PFI regime for major projects or programmes of work. The near-European countries have favoured traditional contracting methods, often based around the FIDIC family of contracts, which are internationally recognised.

In the developing world, project finance may affect how or which consultant and contractors can be employed. For these, the choice of consultant is usually limited to those approved by a financing organisation, and the choice of contractors to those who can finance construction. There are two, possibly inter-related, influences that should also be considered here. First, there may be restrictions (or at least strong influences) on the choice of consultants and contractors on projects that are funded (in whole or in part) from 'development aid' (e.g. Trade for Aid deals). There may also be similar restrictions/influences associated with other forms of project finance (e.g. approvals needed by providers of 'soft finance' from the World Bank, Asian Development Bank, etc.). Second, and separately, there may be tie-ups between consultants and/or contractors and financiers involved in PPP bids.

Sub-contracting

Sub-contracting involves the main contractor entering into legally binding agreements with other contracting organisations to deliver particular packages of work. In civil engineering projects there tends to be three different types of sub-contractor:

- Nominated sub-contractor – the promoter or project manager may directly predetermine sub-contracting arrangements. This is known as 'nomination' and its prime uses are for long lead works or where a particular supplier's product is required, or if novel or risky work is required from a specialist sub-contractor. The process of nomination has fallen out of favour over recent years and this was reflected in the most recent revisions of JCT11 contracts. JCT do not recommended nomination because it complicates relationships and divides responsibilities. Similarly, NEC3 does not specifically provide for nomination in the contracts; this is because all sub-contractors are effectively viewed as 'domestic'.
- Named sub-contractor – 'naming' of sub-contractors enables the promoter to influence rather than predetermine (in the case of nomination) the main contractor's selection of sub-contractors. This is contractually less complicated and the performance of the sub-contractors is usually the responsibility of the main contractor. Common practice is for the promoter to invite potential sub-contractors to tender for work packages. The promoter will evaluate the tenders and then name the short-list of sub-contractors in the main contract documents. 'Naming' has now replaced 'nomination' in JCT contracts.
- Domestic sub-contractor – is any sub-contractor, other than a nominated sub-contractor, that the main contractor enters into an agreement with to carry out part of the construction works. Like with nomination, however, the work of the sub-contractor is the responsibility of the main contractor.

The use of the word 'sub-contactors', or 'subbies', is in decline; increasingly the term 'suppliers' is used to reflect the emergence of 'supply-chain management' principles in the delivery of infrastructure assets. There are many reasons why sub-contracting is used in civil engineering projects, including:

- complexity and scale of the project
- a lack of specific expertise within the main contracting organisation to undertake a particular work package
- as a 'risk transfer' strategy
- to manage labour resource demands and availability
- at the behest of the promoter.

The complexity of major civil engineering infrastructure projects often necessitates sophisticated supply-chain management systems. These systems are often hierarchical 'tiers', typically of three levels, through which suppliers are organised (BIS, 2013):

- Tier 1 suppliers – typically the design team, specialist consultants (structural engineering, geotechnical, etc.) and the main contactor employed by the promoter.
- Tier 2 suppliers – suppliers with a contract to provide services to a Tier 1 supplier, also referred to as sub-contractors.
- Tier 3 suppliers – suppliers with a contract to provide services to a Tier 2 supplier.
- Tier n suppliers – in theory, supply chains can span n number of tiers; this presents challenges for the promoter and the project manager in planning, scheduling and general risk management because it is often difficult to understand and predict how events further down the supply chain will impact upon the project.

Due diligence must be performed throughout the procurement process to ensure that relevant legislation and regulations are complied with, particularly in the case of projects that are governed by the EU procurement rules. There may be additional compulsions arising from 'anti-corruption' or 'public interest' obligations in specific national or more local legal requirements. These may apply both to countries inside the EU (and EU Associates and European Free Trade Association (EFTA) members) and in other parts of the world. Often, there will also be broader principles of law protecting against corruption or unfair competition that may necessitate care in the placing of contracts. There may also be similar restrictions arising from the requirements of project funders (e.g. rules attached to project grants or associated with the mandating of project finance, such as project-specific bond or tax approvals, especially in the USA).

Internal contracts

A promoter may choose to have work constructed by their own maintenance or construction department, known in the UK as *direct labour* or direct works, instead of employing contractors. If so, except in small organisations, the design decisions and the consequent manufacturing, installation and construction work is usually the responsibility of different departments. To make their separate responsibilities clear, the order instructing work to be done may in effect be the equivalent of a contract that specifies the scope, standards and price of the work as if the departments were separate companies. Except that disputes between the departments would be managerial rather than legal problems, these internal 'contracts' can be similar to commercial agreements between organisations.

Historically, local government authorities in the UK tended to use direct labour organisations for small projects and maintenance work. Today, many local authorities have separated off their previous direct labour organisations into 'arm's length' bodies, sometimes then privatising them or contracting out many of their activities. There has also been a similar trend with local authorities' design or engineering and architecture departments, with their technical functions split off from so-called 'client-side' activities and then also floated off or contracted out. In some cases almost the whole of an ex-local authority's engineering department has been taken over by or merged with a firm of consulting engineers. In any event, the advent of compulsory competitive tendering legislation (first introduced for construction, maintenance and highways work by the Local Government, Planning and Land Act 1980) introduced new rules that required these organisations to compete for most work with independent contractors. In 1999, the Local Government Act introduced a new requirement for local authorities to procure projects and services through a 'best value' regime. The legislation states that 'a best value authority must make arrangements to secure continuous improvement in the way in which its functions are exercised, having regard to a combination of economy, efficiency and effectiveness'.

If a contractor promotes as well as carries out a project, they may need to separate these two roles because different expertise and responsibilities are involved in deciding whether to proceed with the project and then how to do it. Separation of these responsibilities may also be required because others are participating in financing the project. For all such projects, except small ones, an internal contract may therefore be appropriate to define responsibilities and liabilities.

Project execution plan and procedures

The results of the decisions taken on the contracting options should be the proposed strategy for a project. The project manager should agree it with all the managers who control resources and obtain the promoter's acceptance of the strategy before proceeding with the project.

Everybody working for the project should be made aware of the strategy, at least to the extent of stating the project objectives and scope. A small guidance note or a display specific to a project can achieve this. For larger or novel projects a 'project execution plan' or 'project implementation plan' and displays are required.

Whether a project needs a detailed separate plan or only a document that supplements established standards and procedures, every person who is to be responsible for planning and managing work for it should be told

■ the promoter's objectives
■ the purpose of the project
■ performance criteria and constraints
■ quality and safety standards required
■ completion date and any intermediate dates of importance to the promoter
■ cost limits
■ the priorities between time, quality and cost
■ the risk and safety management policies, and any special requirements or constraints
■ the organisation of the work – the work breakdown structure and the contract strategy
■ the role and organisation of the project team and supporting resources
■ the system for project communications, control and management.

The execution plan should be used to guide all the work that follows.

FURTHER READING AND REFERENCES

Baden Hellard R (1993) *Total Quality in Construction Projects, Achieving Profitability with Customer Satisfaction*. Thomas Telford, London, UK.

BIS (Department for Business, Innovation and Skills) (2013) *Building a Responsible Payment Culture*. BIS, London, UK. See https://www.gov.uk/government/uploads/system/uploads/attachment_data/file/315462/bis-14-793-building-a-responsible-payment-culture-government-response.pdf (accessed 29 September 2015).

Ford CR, Johnson GC, Douglas HR, Henderson JR and Valentine WH (1997) The Skye Crossing – a design, build, finance and operate project. *Proceedings of the Institution of Civil Engineers – Civil Engineering* **20(2)**: 46–58.

ISO (International Organization for Standardization) (2009) ISO 31000: 2009. Risk management. Principles and guidelines (provides principles, framework and a process for managing risk). ISO, Geneva, Switzerland.

Select Committee on Public Accounts 13th Report (2001) The refinancing of the Fazakerley PFI Prison contract.

Civil Engineering Procedure
ISBN 978-0-7277-6069-2

Chapter 5
Design

Design and the design process

Design is often described as a 'creative' process requiring the professional to draw upon a broad range of 'hard' and 'soft' skills in the resolution of complex engineering problems. In other words, design is a balance of creative, technical and people/social skills. The critical importance of design competence is reflected in the emphasis that all accredited UK higher education degree programmes place upon it. The Joint Board of Moderators (JBM) (the accrediting body of the Institution of Civil Engineers, the Institution of Structural Engineers and the Chartered Institution of Highways and Transportation) requires universities to demonstrate how the principles of design are taught and assessed across all years of study; this is known as the 'design thread' (the other threads are sustainability and health and safety risk/risk assessment). In order to understand the design process better, it is useful to refer to the JBM guidance (2009) as this sets out a number of attributes in a 'competent engineer' from a design perspective:

- An understanding that design is a creative process in which experience and a thorough knowledge of historical precedent can inform both intuition and conscious choice.
- An ability to cope with the uncertainties associated with the multitude of factors making up the design brief. It is rare for a unique solution to emerge, and more commonly there will be any number of possible solutions for which the 'best' solutions will represent an intelligent compromise.
- An ability to 'think outside the box'. Could a better design be achieved if unnecessary constraints (explicit or implicit) in the brief were renegotiated?
- An ability to interact with clients to help both client and other team members develop a better understanding and definition of the brief and the functional, social and economic objectives.
- A knowledge of how to gather relevant information on environmental and planning issues, site conditions, material suppliers, collaborators, specialists and other contractors. All this information is needed to inform the design process.
- An ability to sort and synthesise all information so that proposed solutions can be tested against the criteria identified in the brief and the overall functional, social and economic objectives.

■ Be comfortable working in a system, which enables people to work together, and which allows them to plan and track progress towards a developing solution. This applies to both the sub-components of design and the overall design process.
■ An ability to justify the chosen solution to stakeholders.

The design process takes place over a number of 'stages' or 'phases', the parlance depends on, inter alia, the nature and context of the project, the nature of the promoter and the funding regime. In Chapter 1 there are some examples of project life cycles; these are useful structures through which the design process can be understood. In practice, the interactions between the various design disciplines and actors create a complex environment that can never be fully encapsulated within the largely sequential project life cycle models.

In general, the aim of the designer should be to ensure that sufficient information is produced at each stage of the process (Figure 5.1) to

■ show that the project will achieve the promoter's objectives (quality, time, cost)
■ produce solutions which can be safely delivered
■ obtain any necessary approvals and consents
■ define in detail the next stages of the project, particularly the drawings and specifications needed for contracts, construction, testing and commissioning.

The successful design of a project demands expertise in technical detail alongside a broader understanding of engineering principles, construction methods, cost-planning, health, safety and welfare, legal and environmental considerations and procurement

Figure 5.1 Stages in the whole life of an asset

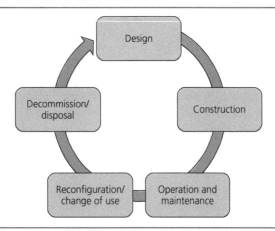

methods. In the case of a river crossing, for example, should the solution be over, under, around or on? What will be the cost, how can it be built, how long will it take, how will it be maintained and what effects will the project have on society and the environment? The resulting information should specify what is to be built, the standards and tests required, health and safety criteria, constraints on construction methods, and the life-long inspection and maintenance requirements.

Design begins at the first stage investigation of ideas for possible solutions to achieve the project scope or brief and becomes progressively more defined through the development of schemes and options. The **RIBA** Plan of Work 2013 provides a good example of the various stages of the design process (this is summarised in Figure 5.2) from a building project perspective. Civil infrastructure projects tend to follow a similar path, although this very much depends on scope and complexity. Generally, the amount of design definition and detail will increase as the design moves through the various stages of the design process. This means that the design resources (people and fees) will accordingly increase.

The design process can proceed rapidly through these stages if the project is of relatively low complexity or similar to previous schemes. It is always the case that approvals from

Figure 5.2 RIBA Plan of Work 2013

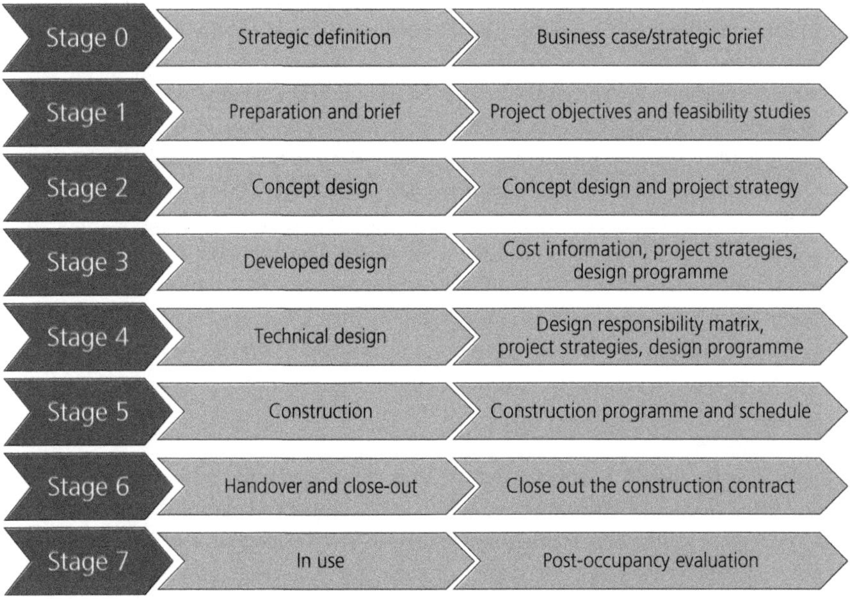

Stage 0	Strategic definition	Business case/strategic brief
Stage 1	Preparation and brief	Project objectives and feasibility studies
Stage 2	Concept design	Concept design and project strategy
Stage 3	Developed design	Cost information, project strategies, design programme
Stage 4	Technical design	Design responsibility matrix, project strategies, design programme
Stage 5	Construction	Construction programme and schedule
Stage 6	Handover and close-out	Close out the construction contract
Stage 7	In use	Post-occupancy evaluation

the promoter, statutory consultees and other appropriate stakeholders will be required before design can progress through key stages or phases. Separate defined stages will be required where the responsibility for design is to pass from one organisation to another. The problem with design in the field of civil engineering (covering vastly different infrastructure and building projects) is that they all have their own processes, procedures and terminology even for UK projects. The challenge lies in understanding and defining the problem(s) and finding appropriate solution(s) to suit. International civil engineering projects will require the designer to understand a range of different regulations, laws and procedures together with a range of local/regional, cultural and political issues.

Design brief or scope
The promoter's project brief should lead to feasibility studies. However, it is not unusual for the brief to be developed or redefined as the project evolves. Designers must advise the promoters or their project managers on the alternative possible schemes that might meet their needs. It is rare that the feasibility stage identifies a single solution/option. The feasibility stage is usually followed by a design development stage (scheme or preliminary design) which seeks to look at the options and agree with the promoter which one provides the best solution to be taken forward into design development and detailed design. The feasibility stage provides the necessary information to inform the design brief. This brief defines the scope, objectives, priorities and design criteria of the proposed project. Some briefs are more specific on the operational aspects of a project – whole life cycle design – others are not as specific on operational issues.

The brief should provide the guidance needed to undertake the preliminary design, and also provide flexibility to develop the most cost-effective solution. Changes to the brief should be made only if the promoter's requirements or information used in the feasibility studies has changed. During the preliminary design the construction techniques and any innovations should be considered along with key safety issues. It is during this stage that the greatest savings can be made to the project costs. The opportunity to make savings diminishes with time and the cost to implement changes increases with time, for example later changes may require re-design, discarding of work done or delays to construction. Many considerations are likely to apply during the stages of the design process. Some of these are explored further in the text that follows.

Design programme
The design brief should ideally include a schedule of dates for delivering the various design stages (including drawings, reports, specifications, calculations), approvals and other information for cost estimating, tendering, contracts and construction. If the project is complex, uncertain or urgent, every stage may need detailed planning and coordination. Elements to be considered include desktop studies, site investigations,

environmental impact studies, risk studies, modelling work, design options, design reviews and checking, cost estimates, approval by the promoter, approval from various authorities, public meetings/consultations, the health and safety plan, preparation or tender and contract information.

The design programme should consider when a contractor is to be appointed and their input to the design. It should give time for the team to visit the site to assess design and construction problems and, if needed, to arrange for sufficient surveys and measurements, investigations and data gathering studies to provide evidence for use in the preparation of appropriate design solutions.

The designer should advise the promoter of the time needed to prepare designs, contract drawings and a specification, as lack of time for these is highly likely to lead to delays, additional expenditure and potential errors. The promoter should advise the designer of any constraints, including the time needed for consents and approvals by the promoter or by the design team. Adequate time should also be provided in the programme to coordinate the various design disciplines. In some forms of procurement, such as construction management and management contracting, professionals other than the designer will take a role in coordination of design data.

Quality–cost–time
Of all the considerations, arguably the most important is the relationship between the quality and performance of the completed project, its cost and the time taken for the work, within the requirements of health and safety. This need to consider these together is illustrated in Figure 5.3.

Directions on balancing the cost, quality and speed of construction should be given in the design brief, as the achievement of one can often conflict with the achievement of the others.

Health, safety and welfare
The health and safety of designers, construction workers, operatives and the general public must be given the highest consideration when designing any project. Therefore, the designer must take health and safety into account when preparing design solutions. Since the publication of the Construction (Design and Management) (CDM) Regulations in 1995, legislation has evolved to promote the importance of a safety-centric approach to the execution of civil engineering projects. Further revisions of the CDM Regulations occurred in 2007 and 2015. The most noticeable changes have centred on the role of the professional (or organisation) responsible for coordination of health and safety information; in the 1995 regulations that was the duty of the 'planning supervisor' and then, in 2007, the role was changed to that of the 'CDM coordinator'. The common

Figure 5.3 Relationship between quality, cost and time

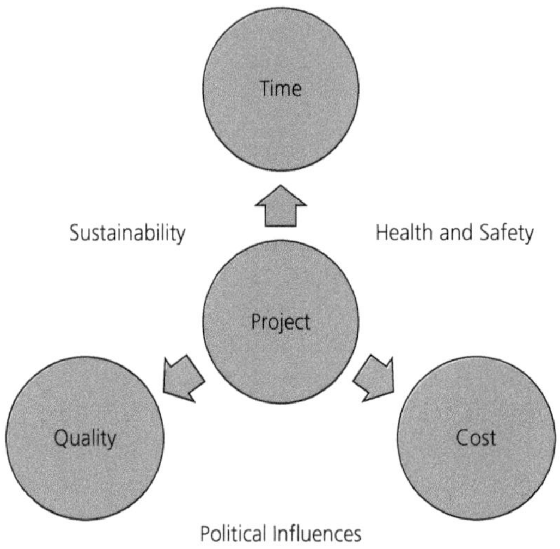

feature in both roles was the tendency for the role to be undertaken by a third party consultant or organisation. With the advent of the CDM Regulations 2015 came the new role of the 'principal designer' to replace the CDM coordinator. The other duty-holders remain: the promoter (client), the principal contractor, designers and contractors.

In the regulations, 'designer' means any person (including a client, contractor or other person referred to in these regulations) who in the course or furtherance of a business

(a) prepares or modifies a design; or
(b) arranges for, or instructs, any person under their control to do so, relating to a structure, or to a product or mechanical or electrical system intended for a particular structure, and a person is deemed to prepare a design where a design is prepared by a person under their control.

CDM 2015 requires the principal designer to

- identify and eliminate or control foreseeable risks
- prepare the health and safety file
- ensure designers carry out their duties
- liaise with the principal contractor to help in the planning, management and monitoring of the construction phase
- prepare and provide relevant information to other duty-holders.

Case study 4: Leeds railway station (south entrance) project

Leeds railway station is the busiest outside of London. In order to meet expected future increases in passenger demand and enhance access for workers and residents in the Holbeck Urban Village area, promoters Network Rail and the West Yorkshire Combined Authority sought designs for a new entrance to the south of the station. The desired location for the new entrance introduced numerous engineering challenges, including the need to work over an existing watercourse and in close proximity to an operational railway. The design solution involved the installation of piled foundations and two concrete piers in the bed of the River Aire to accommodate a transfer deck; and a series of galvanised beams, positioned at 1.8 m centres spanning 10.2 m between the new concrete piers and cantilevered a further 3.5 m beyond the centre line of each pier to provide support to the steel columns above and to create an access and maintenance deck around the perimeter of the building base. The steel for the transfer deck was installed using a 63 m on-site tower crane, which lifted the steel members off barges used to transfer the off-site manufactured components from a loading facility downriver. The use of steel decks was primarily to ease the method of construction and reduce the health and safety hazards associated with working over the river (See Figure 5.4.). The subsequent installation of the steel superstructure frame, which is characterised by a complex geometry – a series of portalised arches at 1.8 m centres – followed a similar construction method; the whole project was very much 'CDM driven'.

Figure 5.4 Leeds station (south entrance) project

The principal designer is responsible for coordinating the pre-construction phase health and safety information. This is most likely to be the lead engineer (or lead architect as appropriate). At the stage where the project moves to site and initial operations commence, the responsibility transfers to the principal contractor/contractor. The role of the principal designer will remain, in most projects, during phases of the construction process – the appointment ceases when design work is no longer undertaken. Where the appointment of the principal designer ends before practical completion, because all design work is complete, the principal designer must ensure that the principal contractor has comprehensive information on the hazards that have not been eliminated in the designs, the means employed to reduce or control those hazards and the implications for implementing the design work during the remainder of the project. The principal designer should also hand over the health and safety file (this is a document that contains 'information necessary for future construction, maintenance, refurbishment or demolition to be carried out safely, and is retained by the promoter or any future owner of the asset').

Sustainability, waste reduction and low-carbon design

Due to the short- and long-term impacts of civil engineering projects, promoters are increasingly demonstrating a commitment to sustainability and the low-carbon economy. Sustainability is defined by the Brundtland Commission's (1987) as 'development which meets the needs of current generations without compromising the ability of future generations to meet their own needs'. It is a broad concept and encapsulates a number of considerations; however, a number of methodologies exist to guide designers, the most common being CEEQUAL. CEEQUAL began life as an environmental impact assessment tool (EIA) but has recently evolved to consider a broader, more holistic approach. The methodology considers nine aspects of a civil engineering project:

- project/contract strategy (optional)
- project/contract management
- people and communities
- land use (above and below water) and landscape
- the historic environment
- ecology and biodiversity
- water environment (fresh and marine)
- physical resources use and management
- transport.

Waste reduction is an important strategic objective in design; the costs and environmental impacts of landfill are increasingly requiring promoters and designers to consider innovative solutions. The Waste and Resources Action Programme (WRAP) has published *Designing out Waste: A Design Team Guide for Civil Engineering* (2010), which provides a practical approach to reduce waste in civil engineering projects. The first part of the two-part approach provides the case for action and details the principles of designing out waste through a structured approach for implementation in civil engineering projects. Designers can use the second part, a 'Technical solutions' guide, which provides summary sheets on a range of design solutions to support design development.

Form and function

The aesthetics of structures and their subsequent performance has been a preoccupation of humanity stretching back to ancient times. The Roman architect and military engineer, Vitruvius, outlined the three integrated principles of good design as strength, usefulness and beauty, in his ancient treatise *The Ten Books on Architecture*. These principles were successively reinterpreted through the ages, and they still persist in definitions of good engineering and architecture. Good design should be robust enough to last for its specified design life and usually beyond it; function well through life; and, ideally, provide some visual delight.

A structure will need to be designed and built to resist the loads it will be exposed to, such as movement (traffic crossing a bridge, for example), the forces of gravity and natural forces (e.g. the wind). Other forces of nature, such as earthquakes and extreme weather events, also have to be designed for in certain regions. Increasingly robust design specifications are demanded to provide resilience to the extreme weather events that are brought about by climate change all over the world. Materials should be resilient enough to withstand the effects of age and so that they weather appropriately with optimal maintenance and repair.

Functionality is implicit in the search for optimum design quality and, although it may not always entirely follow form, it is obviously an integral and essential part of the whole engineering or architectural solution. An inappropriate design solution can unfortunately lead to structural or operational failure, which regrettably could result in loss of life or costly disruption.

To be classed as a 'good design' the outcome must meet the client's expectations – be robust, functional, aesthetically appealing and embrace sustainability. Good engineering and architecture does not rely on the artifice of decorated structure or indeed structural decoration, but transcends these qualities to fuse the three main principles in harmony.

Roles and organisation

The brief should state who will lead the design team, the individual roles and who will be responsible for all the various elements of design work. Specialist design contributions may also be necessary. Multi-disciplinary team working will be effective when there is no confusion of roles and responsibilities.

Under the CDM Regulations 2015, the promoter has a duty to appoint designers who have the competence and resources required to discharge their duties effectively. The design team may include members of the promoter's permanent staff, their project manager or external personnel, specialist firms or contractors employed for consultation and for design of sections of the project. In some cases the designer may be employed by the contractor and not by the promoter. The design of specialist work may be sub-contracted to the main design organisation, but the designer should take all reasonable steps to make sure the design of any sub-consultants is appropriate. Design responsibilities and liabilities is a complex area which inevitably involves the legal and insurance professions. The objective of any design should always be to avoid design errors and mistakes. Reviewing and checking designs is an essential part of the design process.

In an ideal world the design team should be located together, at least for part of the design process. Sometimes on complex projects, some or all of the team may have to move to the project site at the start of construction to provide a smoother transition of the design information into construction.

Outline/concept design

Outline designs giving more information than used for the feasibility study may be required for approval by the promoter, the funders and statutory authorities. If this is the case, the designer should provide the information required by the promoter and for obtaining planning and other approvals and consents. This information is also used by the promoter to provide more detailed information to justify the project proceeding to the next stage.

Planning permission may be granted in one or two stages: first, for an 'outline' submission, which may be accepted subject to conditions, and, second, for a detailed submission, which may also be subject to further information. Time and resources are needed in order to achieve this. The designer should be familiar with all the relevant planning policy documentation before commencing the design and should have regular meetings with the planner throughout the design process to understand and facilitate any planning considerations ahead of submitting a planning application. This is the same for a range of other regulatory bodies that could have a statutory interest in the design solution.

The designer will also have to prepare, or cooperate in the preparation of, an EIA, with evidence that outside parties who may be affected by the project have been consulted and their interests considered. For this and other work that draws on specialist knowledge, the designer has to plan and manage interfaces with other professionals, the public and third parties, in order to obtain information and agree a design that meets the promoter's objectives and priorities. The Engineering Council has published the *UK Standard for Professional Engineering Competence* (2014), which provides engineers with guidance on sustainability issues and also on the need to seek ways to change, improve and integrate designs, methods, operations and so on to improve the environment.

Design development

Designs must be economical to construct. The availability of appropriate resources – materials, labour and plant – for construction is important to the economics of the design, particularly at geographically isolated sites.

The experience of design teams and/or contractors can be invaluable in achieving practical and effective cost and programme solutions. Construction expertise should be applied throughout the design process, rather than alternative designs being received from contractors with their tenders just before construction. Traditionally in the UK, the experience of contractors was brought in only at the tender stage. Consultation with contractors during the design development is preferred by some promoters to ensure that the design is suitable for economic and safe construction. In some cases the contractor is appointed early in the design process, in a process commonly known as early contractor involvement (ECI), but if not the consultations need to be conducted fairly between contractors who may later be competing for a contract to construct the project.

The extent of design information needed for inviting tenders depends on the method for procuring construction. The designer should discuss the most appropriate procurement route and contract type with the promoter and his or her other advisers in good time for the designer to be able to produce the type and extent of the documents required for inviting tenders.

In the traditional procedure, the detailed design of a project should be completed before tenders for construction are invited. If contractors are being invited to be responsible for detailed design as well as construction, the promoter's designer should assist in their pre-qualification, tender analysis and selection. Only outline design drawings and performance specifications may be needed for inviting tenders where the contractor is to take the responsibility for delivering the detailed design, but the promoter will usually employ a design team to check the designs submitted by the contractor.

Some site or other information may be known only when construction is under way and in such cases, redesign or supplementary design work during the construction phase may be unavoidable. Typical reasons for this are:

- excavation in ground which proves to be different from that inferred from site investigations
- structures to house equipment, the details of which are unknown at the design stage
- the promotor changes the scope.

Sometimes it is not possible to gather site investigation or survey information because access to some areas of the site is restricted due to operational reasons.

Design for whole-life cost

Promoters are increasingly concerned with the whole-life costs of design decisions. Designers will often seek specialist advice from civil engineers or cost consultants to assist with optimising design solutions. The designer will often be challenged to strike the right balance between capital cost and operational/maintenance costs over a predetermined time frame. This requires the use of specific techniques that are variously described in ISO 15686-5 (ISO, 2008a) and in the supporting guide PD 156865 (BSI, 2008b). Design for whole-life cost is widely viewed as a suitable approach to meeting the demands for value for money compliance, particularly in projects for local authorities (see 'best value authorities', Local Government Act 2009) and credit for undertaking whole-life cost analysis is recognised in sustainability assessment tools such as CEEQUAL and BREEAM.

Operation and maintenance

The operation and maintenance costs should be considered early so that the design can incorporate details which optimise both the efficient running and maintenance of the facility. The designer should also consider how the facility can be operated and maintained in a safe manner. The promoter should have a big say in how the facility should be operated and maintained. Ideally, the promoter's experienced operational and maintenance staff should be consulted for their requirements for access to inspect, maintain and replace structures, materials or equipment throughout the life of the facility. Generally, an operating and maintenance (O&M) manual will be produced by the designer to help the staff operating and maintaining the facility to do so in the most appropriate way. Designs that use standard materials and components make replacements more cost-effective and easier to obtain. This can be important to the promoter, not only to permit quick recovery in emergency situations, but also to obtain more components for a later expansion of the facility.

Decommissioning/disposal

All civil engineering projects should have a specified design life, e.g. many building structures have a design life of 60 years where as a bridge will typically be 120 years. In reality, such structures will often be maintained long beyond their original design life. Designs have inherently finite lives and, at some stage, will require to be decommissioned and/or demolished. The designer can prepare for this by, for example, ensuring that structural frames are easily identifiable, specifying construction procedures that may be easily reversed, specifying materials that can be recycled or that generate low quantities of waste, and incorporating quality features into equipment design to safeguard against spillages of potential contaminants during operation. The CDM Regulations

2015 place a requirement on the principal designer to ensure that the design enables the processes of decommissioning in a safe manner.

Statutory approvals

All designs require a number of approvals (in addition to those approval stages required by the promoter). These approvals must be incorporated into the design and construction programme and sufficient time should be allocated for the designer to develop solutions and discuss them with the relevant approving authority and for any statutory time periods for the approving authority to make a decision. Some of these approvals can take many months and sometimes years to achieve and can consequently dictate the programme for the project. Gaining all the appropriate approvals is an essential part of the design process.

The designer may need to present the design to the promoter and planning representatives of statutory authorities (also known as statutory consultees), the public and others for their comments and approval. In order to secure approval, the designer should understand the nature of objections to proposals and gain acceptance of the final design through appropriate stakeholder management. On a large, novel or particularly controversial project, this process may be undertaken over several iterations before an agreed resolution can be achieved.

The designer must possess appropriate skills and confidence in conveying complex technical information to a wider audience. Moreover, the designer should be aware of when key consultation events/presentations will take place and when deadlines for submission of appropriate documents are set.

Some schemes require detailed statutory orders for the compulsory purchase of land or changes to existing statutory rights. A decision may be required by the Secretary of State and in some cases an Act of Parliament may be required. Recent high-profile examples include Crossrail and High Speed 2. These procedures invariably take years and require a substantial amount of design, documentation and preparation. The scope and detail of the outline design may therefore be greatly increased. The designer should provide the information required for the promoter to present their case and obtain the necessary approvals.

Additional consents and approvals may be required from other statutory bodies, such as utility companies or environmental bodies. Outline approvals and cost estimates sufficient to proceed to construction may be obtained based on the outline design. Detailed approval may follow later. Again, the designer should provide the promoter with the information required. In some cases the contractor may obtain the detailed approval.

Different counties have difference procedures and approval processes and it is essential that a designer is familiar with such processes and approvals before starting any design work – this is particularly the case for infrastructure projects.

Detailed design

The design development stage advances the design to provide the contractor with sufficient information to allow the design to be costed and ultimately constructed. This stage involves preparing detailed design drawing, specification and tender documentation. Generally, the completed detailed design should have a final pre-tender cost estimate before being sent to contractors for a tender price. This re-estimate can be used to judge tenderers' prices.

Once the detailed design has started, changes should be allowed only if essential for the satisfactory completion of the project as changes inevitably increase costs and time. A change control procedure should be applied so that the total potential costs and time effects of any proposed change might be determined.

The designer should be expert on specifying materials, recognising that ongoing research and development regularly yields new products. The engineering properties of materials should be understood and development work should be undertaken if needed to test new materials and methods (provided that this can be accommodated in the programme).

Standardised and locally sourced materials and components should be chosen wherever suitable, in order to reduce construction costs, improve logistics and save training of construction employees. Innovations in construction methods and materials should, therefore, be considered early in design, in time to investigate their advantages to the promoter's objectives. Any potential downside risks associated with innovative solutions and products should be explored with the promoter as part of the risk management process. At the detailed stage it is wise to use proven technology, methods and materials for all time-critical aspects of a project.

Design methods

Calculation and analysis

The early stages of the design process should identify the likely form and interdependence of the main elements of the project. Generally, experienced designers can move quickly and efficiently to likely solutions using approximate loadings and associated design calculations. Established standards and guides should be used wherever appropriate, to achieve reliable results economically.

During the detailed design stage more accurate and refined loadings, calculations and analysis are carried out in order to make sure the designs are safe, efficient and economical. At this stage it is also important that the various multi-disciplinary elements of the design are brought together in a coordinated manner to make sure that the final solution is a holistic solution. The detailed design stage should articulate to the promoter and the approval authorities a design solution that can be constructed safely and within the promoter's budget and timescale to the right quality and with minimum impact on the environment.

Reviewing, checking and assessment

All designs should be reviewed and checked. Experienced professionals should undertake design reviews in order that a degree of challenge to the proposals produced by the design team exists – this should enable iteration to a design solution that is the most appropriate. The assumptions and methodology employed in the design should form part of the review.

It is essential that all designs are checked; this is a key part of the design process and is usually documented separately. The level of checking will depend on the significance of the element of the design being checked – ranging from self-checking, to checking by another member of the same organisation, to checking by an independent organisation. Checking designs by an independent party is statutorily required for certain structures, for example bridges and dams. All checking should be formally recorded in the design files and on every drawing, specification and set of calculations.

Value management and value engineering

Value management provides a framework for the critical analysis of a project outcome by focusing on how the outcome will be achieved. BS EN 12973: 2000 (BSI, 2000) sets out the generic processes and identifies a range of tools and techniques that are available as part of a value management approach. The standard describes processes that can be used to review the primary benefits, outcomes and needs of the total project, as valued by the promoter, to test whether the total project will best achieve the desired commercial or non-commercial objectives.

In contrast, value engineering techniques form part of a broader approach to value management that embraces a range of qualitative and quantitative techniques, such as the widely used Function Analysis System Technique (FAST). Value engineering is an analytical technique for questioning whether the scope of a design and the quality of the proposed elements of the design will achieve the project's objectives at the optimum cost. It can be used at every stage of the design process and provides an opportunity for the designer to prove that design choices are justified economically. Value engineering techniques generally focus on specific elements of the project rather than the total project and seek to test that such elements are delivered in the most cost-effective and timely manner to achieve the agreed quality level.

Review and audit

Depending upon the project's strategy on risks, the design process may also be monitored by independent review and audit. The application of a quality assurance policy may require audits during any stage of the design process. The designer needs to allow time for these audits and for any repetition of work shown to be necessary.

Building information modelling (BIM)

Modern software advances enable the design team to utlitise 3D, 4D (time) and 5D (cost) data in such a way that alternative solutions, design coordination, checking clearances for construction, operations and maintenance, presenting the design, 'taking off' quantities and revising detail can be readily achieved. Other tools are available to test the critical load conditions and examine factors of safety. The designer must understand how the software employed operates, in order to be confident that the results are accurate. The designer must not lose the skill to apply engineering principles to determine solutions, and should seek to validate the operation of software used and verify computed solutions. We look at the concepts of BIM in greater detail in Chapter 11.

Construction support

The designer role on site depends on the requirements of the project, the form of contract and the promoter. The designer should make recommendations to the promoter about the level of support that should be provided on site to help the promoter make sure the design is constructed in accordance with the design drawings and specifications. The designer may provide support from the design office or may be based on site. Any role that requires a level of site supervision should be agreed with the promoter, documented and communicated to all stakeholders.

The designer may be required to carry out any or all of the following roles:

- resolving design queries and offering redesign, especially if unforeseen conditions are encountered
- checking that the assumptions made during the design are encountered on site
- reviewing and approving design carried out by the contractor or sub-contractors, at least for temporary works, which are the contractor's responsibility
- specifying any additional tests and assessing the results
- assisting in producing the as-built drawings
- witnessing testing and commissioning of the works.

Depending on the form of contract, the designer may have the role of administrating the contact on behalf of the promoter.

Ethical conduct

Civil engineers make a significant contribution to shaping modern society and with this comes a responsibility to act ethically at all times. The ICE requires all members to adhere to its Code of Professional Conduct (ICE, 2004). This sets out and defines the ethical standards that should guide all decisions and actions that members take. The code covers six main themes:

- Discharge professional duties with **integrity**.
- Undertake work at one's level of **competence**.
- Have full regard for the public interest.
- Show regard for the environment and for the **sustainable** management of natural resources.
- Commit to **continuing professional development (CPD)**.
- **Notify** if convicted of a criminal offence or upon bankruptcy, and report misconduct by another member.

In addition to the Code of Professional Conduct, ICE members must follow the Institution's guidance on bribery and corruption, and equality and diversity.

From a design perspective, some considerations for the practising engineer include:

- Does the design introduce hazards that may bring workers and site operatives into harm's way? Can these be designed out?
- Does the design impact negatively on the local physical and natural environment? Can these impacts be minimised?
- Is the promoter aware of their duty to provide information under the CDM Regulations 2015? How can the quality of this information be reviewed and acted upon?
- Are current regulations, codes of practice and statutory provisions relevant to the project being considered and reflected in the design?
- Is the designer adequately insured (professional indemnity cover) to undertake the work?

FURTHER READING AND REFERENCES

BSI (2000) BS EN 12973:2000. Value management. BSI, London, UK.

BSI (2008) PD 156865 Standardized method of life cycle costing for construction procurement. A supplement to BS ISO 15686-5: 2008. Buildings and constructed assets. Service life planning. Life cycle costing. ISO, Geneva, Switzerland.

Engineering Council (UK) (2014) *The UK Standard for Professional Engineering Competence (UK-SPEC)*. ICE, London, UK. http://www.engc.org.uk/standards-guidance/standards/uk-spec/ (accessed 17 August 2015).

ICE (Institution of Civil Engineers) (2004) ICE Code of Professional Conduct. https://www.ice.org.uk/ICEDevelopmentWebPortal/media/Documents/About%20Us/ice-code-of-professional-conduct.pdf (accessed 29 September 2015).

ICE (2014) *Civil Engineering Ethics Toolkit*. ICE, London, UK. https://www.ice.org.uk/disciplines-and-resources/best-practice/civil-engineering-ethics-toolkit (accessed 17 August 2015).

ISO (International Organization for Standardization) (2008) ISO 15686-5: 2008. Building and constructed assets – Service life planning – Part 5: Life-cycle costing. ISO, Geneva, Switzerland.

JBM (Joint Board of Moderators) (2009) *Degree Guidelines – Annex B (Design in Degree Programmes)*. http://www.jbm.org.uk/uploads/JBM122_AnnexBDesign.pdf (accessed 17 August 2015).

WRAP (2010) *Designing out Waste: A Design Team Guide for Civil Engineering*. WRAP, Banbury, UK. http://www2.wrap.org.uk/downloads/Designing_out_Waste_-_a_design_team_guide_for_civil_engineering_-_Part_1_interactive_1.eb71d8e8.9111.pdf (accessed 17 August 2015).

Civil Engineering Procedure
ISBN 978-0-7277-6069-2

ICE Publishing: All rights reserved
http://dx.doi.org/10.1680/cep.60692.073

Chapter 6
Civil engineering construction contracts

Principles of contract

The contract is the most important document in a civil engineering project. A range of contract options exist and decisions on selection of the most appropriate form should reflect the project requirements. The promoter's priorities on time/cost/quality and an analysis of how they can be achieved must also feature in the detail of the contract; the underlying division of obligations, responsibilities and rewards, and its general approach to risk sharing and dispute resolution. Where the division lies between these broad features of the contract and its specific detailed provisions may not be that easy to determine. The promoter's level of involvement in the design and construction process and the extent to which the design is likely to change during construction are other key considerations.

It is appropriate to start with some consideration of the basic principles of contract in UK law. A contract is an agreement that is enforceable by law and there are three basic principles to consider in formation of one:

1 **an offer and acceptance** that are legally certain (for construction contracts this will usually require certainty as to the works to be carried out, the payment to be made (or at least the basis for assessing payment), the time period for carrying out the works and any other essential requirements)
2 some form of '**consideration**' (essentially something that constitutes value – normally a monetary sum, but a promise to perform another obligation may suffice)
3 an intention to create **legal relations** (this is normally implied in a business setting and in construction contracts this would normally be a given).

Provided that these principles are observed, it is perfectly possible to have an oral contract. Furthermore, a contract may be implied where, although a formal contract has not been drawn up and signed by both parties, there is sufficient certainty as to what obligations each party is to perform and one party provides 'consideration' by, for example, starting the relevant performance.

Accordingly, care needs to be taken in issuing letters, emails or other forms of written communication, asking contractors or construction professionals to carry out work if it is not intended to create a binding contract at the time the letter is issued. Equally important is not commencing work on the basis of a letter/email, etc. assuming that this would form the basis of a contract.

Contract contents

Contracts should specify the scope, location, quality and type of work to be carried out, any time period within which the relevant work is to be carried out and the relevant payment terms. With regard to the latter, the contract must provide an adequate mechanism for determining what payments become due under the contract, and when. Statutory payment mechanisms are principally dealt with under the Housing Grants, Construction and Regeneration Act 1996 and the Local Democracy, Economic Development and Construction Act 2009.

Contracts will usually seek to deal with the occurrence of foreseeable events beyond the control of the contractor and/or the promoter and will usually list risks that may occur during the contract period that will entitle the contractor to seek additional payment and/or extensions of time to any date for completion.

Contracts should also establish:

- Who is responsible for design, construction and supporting work.
- How risks are shared between promoter and contractor.
- Entitlement and any formalities relating to the use of sub-contractors.
- Programmes of work and dates for completion, together with provisions for any agreed extensions of time if the contract specifies an expected completion date, regardless of whether or not there is a requirement for the payment of liquidated damages.
- Insurance arrangements.
- Terms of payment.
- Variations to the works to be carried out.
- Grounds for termination of the contract itself and possibly for the termination of the employment of the contractor (in which case, the contract itself will continue, with the promoter being entitled to appoint a replacement contractor to complete the works and contra-charge the original contractor for any additional costs).
- The settlement of disputes.

Standard forms of construction contract

Standard or 'model' forms of construction contract have been published by a variety of institutions since World War II. Historically, there has been a distinction between the standard forms of contract issued for different types of work. The Joint Contracts

Tribunal (JCT) has published contracts primarily intended for use in connection with building works while the Institution of Civil Engineers (ICE) has produced standard forms of contract primarily intended for engineering works/infrastructure projects. While many of the terms within the different suites of contract have been broadly similar, some features have remained distinctive. For example, under JCT contracts, ground conditions are usually a risk of the contractor. Typically, the known ground conditions are shared with the contractor and any unforeseen conditions are likely to attract extra payment. Additional investigations may also be their responsibility. In contrast, under the former ICE Conditions of Contract, ground conditions have traditionally been a risk of the promoter and give a contractor entitlement to compensation. In practice all civil engineering projects (especially roads) have ground investigation carried out as part of the project planning and feasibility stages. This information is then made available to the contractor at the tender stage and if the actual conditions differ the contractor may have a right to additional time/money (depending on exact contract wording) to carry out further investigations. More recently, under the new Eurocodes a particular type of report may be written and provided to the contractor – a geotechnical baseline report (GBR) – which has a simple purpose of establishing the ground conditions that a contractor relies upon commercially, and any deviation from that leads to additional time/costs.

In more recent years, there has been a blurring of the traditional distinction between the forms of contract for building and engineering works with contracts such as the NEC3 suite and the JCT-Constructing Excellence Contract being applicable to both disciplines. NEC3 has evolved to provide contracts, guidance notes and flow charts and now provides contracts for the acquisition of goods, professional services and works.

Notwithstanding this, there has been a tendency in the construction industry for some promoters to produce their own bespoke amendments to whichever standard form of contract they are using. For example, Network Rail has developed a range of 'amendments' to the former ICE Conditions of Contract (now re-issued as the Infrastructure Conditions of Contract (ICC)), JCT Design and Build Contract and the IMechE/IET MF/1 contract (see later in this chapter). Care needs to be taken that the amending documents remain clearly drafted and their provisions are mutually consistent with those of the rest of the standard form of contract to which they are being applied. From a financial and practical point of view, promoters and other parties to the contract need to be aware of the potential effect of risk pricing if contract terms are amended in their favour.

Following the influential reports of Sir Michael Latham (1994) and Sir John Egan (1998) there has been a movement towards the development of more 'collaborative' forms of contract, specifically the NEC suite of contracts, the ACA Project Partnering Contract (PPC 2000) and the JCT-Constructing Excellence Contract. All these contracts seek to establish, in addition to the usual construction obligations, an obligation on the parties to act collaboratively and consider the interface between members of a project team with each other.

Care is required to select a form of contract that is appropriate to the proposed procurement approach and requirements. If a promoter is seeking to set up a collaborative approach, one of the collaborative forms of contract is best used. On the other hand, if a promoter does not want to manage a design team, a design and build approach may be more appropriate.

With the NEC3, PPC and JCT-Constructing Excellence Contract it is possible to use the same contract documents with different procurement approaches (the contract documents can be completed in a number of different ways, to fit the chosen approach), whereas with some of the more traditional contracts there may be different forms for different procurement approaches.

Publishing bodies for the standard forms of construction contract

The Institution of Civil Engineers (ICE)

The ICE Conditions of Contract were a family of well-established contracts for use on civil engineering schemes. The first edition of the ICE Conditions of Contract (ICE CoC) emerged in 1945, in association with the Federation of Civil Engineering Contractors (now the Civil Engineering Contractors' Association (CECA)). Subsequent editions followed in association with CECA and the Association for Consultancy and Engineering (ACE), most recently the 5th (1973), the 6th (1991) and the 7th (1999) editions.

In 2011, the ICE ceased endorsement of the Conditions of Contract, but they were subsequently relaunched as the Infrastructure Conditions of Contract (published by CECA and ACE), reflecting the prevailing legislation in the Local Democracy, Economic Development and Construction Act 2009. Since 2011, the ICE has endorsed the *New Engineering Contract* third edition (NEC3) suite of contracts.

The NEC contract was initially conceived as 'project management' centric in terms of procedures of cost and programme management. At the time of its issue, it was considered to be radical and was very different to the other standard forms of engineering contract, not least because of its use of 'plain English' language – it was, and remains, written almost exclusively in the present tense, even when indicating matters that are intended to take place in the future. The Latham Report in 1994 considered the contract to be the best of the then standard forms of construction contract and expressed the hope that the large number of standard forms of construction contract would reduce. The ICE issued a new edition entitled the 'NEC Engineering and Construction Contract' in 1995, which addressed the two areas in which the Latham Report considered it to be slightly lacking. The latest edition has become widely used in the public and private sectors in the UK and increasingly so internationally.

The NEC3 suite is comprised of the principal contract 'The Engineering and Construction Contract' (ECC) with a series of 'main options' that are designed to support the particular features of a civil engineering project.

- **Option A – Priced contract with activity schedule**
  Option A creates a straightforward lump-sum form of contract. The activity schedule describes the work that the contractor will undertake to complete the works. The contractor is responsible for estimating the quantities and resources, and for assessing and pricing risks against the activity schedule as a lump sum. The lump sum is adjusted if and when compensation events occur; these are situations where the contractor is required to undertake additional work that falls outside the scope of the contract. There are 19 defined compensation events in NEC3; additional compensation events can be incorporated into the contract by way of 'Z clauses'.

- **Option B – Priced contract with bill of quantities**
  Option B is essentially a 'remeasurement contract' and requires a bill of quantity (BoQ) rather than an activity schedule as the basis for pricing the contract. BoQs are usually prepared by a quantity surveyor and provide measured quantities of the items of work described in the drawings and specifications provided by the promoter. The contractor prices the works based on the BoQ. On completion of the works, if it is found by remeasurement that the estimated quantities were incorrect, the remeasurement determines the additional payment made to the contractor.

- **Option C – Target cost contract with activity schedule**
  Option C creates a 'cost-reimbursable' contract and is perhaps one of the most commonly used NEC3 main options in the UK. The contractor negotiates a 'target price' based on an activity schedule. The activity schedule is priced as a lump sum and the initial target price includes fees for sub-contracts. The key difference with Option C (when contrasted with A and B) is that during the execution of the contract, the risks of cost savings or cost overruns are shared on an agreed portion between the contractor and the promoter. The sharing of risk through a target cost approach is designed to enhance collaboration and motivate improved dispute resolution.

- **Option D – Target cost contract with bill of quantities**
  Option D is similar to Option C, but the use of a BoQ rather than an activity schedule places greater risk with the promoter.

- **Option E – Cost reimbursable contract**
  This option tends to be used for urgent or emergency projects or where the scope of the work required cannot be fully detailed upon execution of the contract. The contractor is reimbursed for all costs incurred plus a fee.

■ **Option F – Management contract**
Option F is also a cost reimbursable contract but is used for projects where sub-contractors undertake the majority of the work. It is therefore suitable for management contracting and construction management procurement arrangements.

In addition to the main options, a series of secondary option clauses is available to accommodate particular risks and uncertainties associated with a project – details of these can be found in Appendix A.

The Joint Contracts Tribunal

The JCT is composed of a number of organisations, representing promoters, contractors, engineers, architects and cost consultants, and has been producing standard forms of contract since 1931. The main form has been the Standard Form of Contract which has been published in a number of different editions and codified as its Standard Building Contract. The 2011 version comprises inter alia:

■ With Quantities
■ With Approximate Quantities
■ Without Quantities.

The Standard Building Contract is also part of a wider suite of contracts comprising inter alia:

■ Minor Works
■ Intermediate Contract
■ Major Project Contract
■ Management Building Contract
■ Construction Management Contract.

JCT also published the 2011 Constructing Excellence Contract. In perhaps a similar way to the difference between the ICE traditional forms of contract and the NEC suite of contracts, the Constructing Excellence Contract is markedly shorter and easier to read than the traditional forms of JCT contract.

Fédération Internationale des Ingénieurs-Conseils (FIDIC)

The International Federation of Consulting Engineers, known as FIDIC, publishes engineering and building contracts primarily intended for use in relation to international construction projects. Appendix A provides an exhaustive list of FIDIC contracts, the main ones being:

■ The Green Book: a short form of contract for engineering and building work of relatively small capital value.

- The Red Book: Conditions of Contract for building and engineering works designed by the promoter.
- The Yellow Book: Conditions of Contract for plant and design-build for electrical and mechanical plant and for building and engineering works designed by the contractor.
- The Silver Book: Conditions of Contract for EPC and turnkey projects.
- The White Book: Client/Consultant Model Services Agreement.

FIDIC also publishes some unique contracts which cover specific activities, such as dredging and tunnelling.

These FIDIC Conditions of Contract, unlike most forms of domestic construction contracts used in the UK, place the majority of the risk of project delivery on the contractor. This is an accepted bias in the world of international projects, where the promoter often expects to receive the outcome contracted for without having to get involved in the detailed management of a project.

There are a number of other professional bodies that publish standard forms of contract for use in relation to projects involving the installation of specialist process plant and related equipment. Projects will usually involve building works but these are often of far less value than, and ancillary to, the plant being installed in the relevant buildings. As a result, greater attention is focused in the contract documents on pre-installation testing and subsequent commissioning. These include:

The Institution of Chemical Engineers (IChemE) forms of contract

- 'Main contract' forms (Red, Green and Burgundy Books) drafted with different risk/payment regimes.
- Sub-contracts (Yellow and Brown Books) drafted with provisions that work 'back-to-back' with the main contracts.
- The Orange Book, a standalone contract intended for carrying out minor works to an existing plant.
- Formal dispute resolution procedures should a dispute arise during the course of a project.

The Institution of Mechanical Engineers (IMechE) and the Institution of Engineering and Technology (IET)

The IMechE, jointly with the IET, issues model forms (with forms of tender, agreement and performance bond included) and a series of supplementary guides.

- MF/1 (Revision 6) 2014 edition
  Model form of contract for the design, supply and installation of electrical,

electronic and mechanical plant: including special conditions for the ancillary development of software.

■ MF/2 (Revision 1) 1999 edition
Home or overseas contracts for the supply of electrical, electronic or mechanical plant: including forms of tender, agreement, sub-contract, supervision contract, performance bond and defects liability demand guarantee.

■ MF/3 (Revision 1) 2001 edition
Home contracts for the supply of electrical and mechanical goods.

■ MF/4 2003 edition
Home or overseas agreements for the provision of consultancy services by engineering consultants.

Standard form of contract for PFI and PPP projects

During recent years there has been a move towards the greater standardisation of contracts under the Private Finance Initiative. The UK Treasury published standard contractual terms for PFI projects (SoPC4), which set out the standard approach to risk allocation between the public and private sectors and includes mandatory principles and drafting for certain key contractual clauses.

In December 2012 the UK government published *A New Approach to Public Private Partnerships*. This introduced a new approach called PF2, the successor to PFI for the delivery of infrastructure and services through public private partnerships (PPP). As a result of this, SoPC4 is replaced by new standard forms of contract applying PF2 requirements. The range of PPP contractual arrangements has developed over time, though all tend to involve the private sector accepting the majority of the risk of project delivery with arrangements for the provision of services and the sharing of risks beyond the construction period. The contractual structures are often referred to by different acronyms, such as BOO (build, own and operate), BOOT (build, own, operate and transfer), DBOM (design, build, operate and maintain), DBFM (design, build, finance, and maintain) and DBFO (design, build, finance and operate). All future use of such structures within the UK will most probably have to conform to the requirements of the PF2 user guide published by HM Treasury.

Underlying considerations for successful contracts

While all construction contracts need to be clear and relevant to the works being carried out, promoters and their advisers need to have in mind the underlying considerations of value/functionality, risk and cost.

Increasing value/functionality

The 'value' or functionality that a construction project will bring to a promoter requires not simply consideration of the capital costs of construction, but also of the whole-life cost of owning and operating a building, structure or item of plant as well as consideration of how the new building/structure adds to the achievement of the promoter's business. Consider the example of the call centre operator who achieved a quantum leap in the performance of the business not by simply improving the efficiency of the construction of the buildings but by re-engineering the layout of the buildings so that they were more enjoyable places to work in. Although the capital cost of the buildings increased by a small fraction, the resulting reduction in staff turnover reduced overall business costs by a much larger fraction.

Historically, the construction industry has concentrated almost exclusively on the initial cost of projects and (as is explained in the following section), more particularly, on the *price* of construction projects.

Risk and cost/price

The issues of risk and price have traditionally not been properly separated. Historically, promoters have amended contracts to pass greater risk to contractors without considering the effect this may have on the contractor's pricing of the works to be carried out. Increasingly, promoters are coming to recognise that passing risk usually has a cost consequence. Sometimes this is recognised and accepted as a worthwhile trade-off for not having to manage a particular risk. However, the level of risk pricing is often not clearly understood, with the result that sometimes promoters do not realise the hidden additional costs they are paying for passing risks, which they might themselves be able to manage effectively at less cost.

For example, under building (as distinct from civil engineering) contracts, the risk of ground conditions is often considered to be an appropriate risk for contractors to manage. If a contractor is not entitled under the contract terms to compensation for the occurrence of adverse unforeseen ground conditions, it is likely that they will include in their tender price some risk contingency to cover the potential of this risk occurring. If the amount of this risk contingency is disclosed, in many situations promoters might prefer to do something about reducing the amount of the contingency or removing it entirely by taking on themselves responsibility for unforeseen ground conditions. Accordingly, it is suggested that a better, more cost-effective, approach may be to try to identify the major risks affecting a project and do something to mitigate them before asking a contractor to price for them. For example, obtaining ground investigation reports in advance of entering into the contract may provide both contractor and promoter with a greater understanding of the potential risks and the appropriate level of contingency. It is standard practice to make available to tendering parties ground investigation data which will have been gathered for: (a) decision to purchase/define land (contamination, general ground strata) and (b) prepare design.

Figure 6.1 Components of overall contractor's price

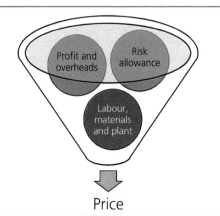

Price

The construction industry is used to dealing in 'prices' (see Figure 6.1), which will in fact include separate elements in respect of:

- profit and overheads
- a risk allowance
- the actual cost of labour, plant and materials.

Often, the distinction between the three elements is blurred and, as a result, rather than starting from an understanding of the actual cost of the works, and building up an understanding of the risk contingency appropriate for a particular project (with a profit margin on top), prices are often calculated on the basis of composite prices based from previous similar projects. There is a great deal of data within the construction industry regarding prices for different forms of activity but far less information regarding actual costs, for both initial costs and especially for whole-life costs.

In an attempt to encourage the discipline of distinguishing between the three elements, some modern forms of contract seek to adopt payment by reference to 'actual cost' rather than valuation by reference to rates and prices for different types of work.

Letting construction contracts

The choice of the form of contract to be used for a particular project is usually made by the promoter (with or without input from its advisers).

Traditionally, the majority of construction contracts have been tendered, with prospective contractors responding by providing the information called for in the invitation to tender, usually a price or schedule of unit prices, a programme and any required design proposals or, when invited to do so, suggested variations to the proposed design. This information is given on the basis of the contractors accepting the specified form of contract stated in the invitation to tender. However, when promoters are seeking to set up collaborative arrangements, most contractors will discuss, object to or even refuse certain conditions within a contract. Negotiations, although often lengthy, can have the advantage of allowing greater consideration of underlying risks and ways of removing or mitigating them before asking contractors to price for work. Even in tender situations, it may be possible or even advantageous for the promoter to request different prices for different allocations of risk, which may at least provide a greater understanding of potential risk pricing.

Ancillary issues
Collateral warranties
Collateral warranties are intended to create contractual obligations between parties who would not otherwise be in direct contract. In the case of a promoter engaging a main contractor, the promoter will obviously be in direct contact with the contractor, but will not be in a direct contractual relationship with the contractor's sub-contractors. However, by entering into a collateral warranty with the sub-contractors, the promoter can obtain a contractual remedy directly against the sub-contractors in the event of breach of the collateral warranty.

Collateral warranties traditionally contain a statement or 'warranty' that the party giving them has performed the terms of their relevant contract (be it professional appointment or construction contract). There is usually also an obligation to maintain a minimum level of professional indemnity insurance to provide comfort to the party receiving the warranty that the party giving the warranty has insurance backing for any claim made under the warranty.

Following the Contracts (Rights of Third Parties) Act 1999 (as amended), it is possible to create rights in favour of third parties to a contract without the necessity to enter into separate collateral warranty arrangements. However, in practice, third party rights are generally excluded in most contractual relationships.

Security for performance
Liquidated or ascertained damages (LADs)
Contracts generally include a provision for the contractor to pay a sum to the promoter in the event of non-performance. Typically, this will relate to the date at which the contract should be completed.

LADs are agreed at the execution of the contract and based on a calculation of the likely loss to the promoter and usually are determined on a fixed daily or weekly sum. The method of calculation is formally documented and must be agreed before project execution.

Performance bonds

Performance bonds may be requested from contractors or sub-contractors to provide security for the performance of their respective contractual obligations. If these are used, they only come into effect if a contractor goes into liquidation; for example, ICC contracts require a 10% bond, which helps fund the additional costs to the promotor if the contractor goes into liquidation. A performance bond will usually be provided by a bank or insurance company and will usually be limited to a percentage of the value of the works being carried out under the relevant contract. There is a cost in providing a performance bond, which is usually passed to the recipient as part of the works costs. Nowadays, performance bonds will not be payable 'on demand'; instead, the recipient of the bond will need to demonstrate that loss has been suffered as a result of breach of the relevant contract. Sometimes, depending on the wording of the bond, this may require proof by way of an adjudication or court order that a breach of contract has occurred and that a specific sum of compensation is now due.

Parent company guarantees

Parent company guarantees may be requested from contractors and/or sub-contractors where they are subsidiaries to a larger parent company. Liability under parent company guarantees may be expressly limited but often is not.

FURTHER READING AND REFERENCES

Broome J (2012) *NEC3: A User's Guide*. ICE Publishing, London, UK.

Egan J (1998) *Rethinking Construction: Report of the Construction Task Force*. HMSO, London, UK.

HMG (Her Majesty's Government) (1998) *Scheme for Construction Contracts (England and Wales) Regulations 1998*. The Stationery Office, London, UK, Statutory Instrument 1998 No. 649.

ICE (Institution of Civil Engineers) (1999) *Conditions of Contract*, 7th edn. Thomas Telford, London, UK.

JCT (Joint Contracts Tribunal) (2011) *Constructing Excellence Contract*. Joint Contracts Tribunal, London, UK.

Latham M (1994) *Constructing the Team*. HMSO, London, UK.

McAleenan C and Oloke D (eds) (2015) *ICE Manual of Health and Safety in Construction*, 2nd edn. ICE Publishing, London, UK.

Murdoch J and Hughes W (2007) *Construction Contracts: Law and Management*. Taylor & Francis, Oxford, UK.

New Engineering Contract, 3rd edn (2009) Thomas Telford, London, UK.

PPC 2000 (Amended 2013) ACA standard form of contract for project partnering, ACA Publishing, Horsham, UK.

Civil Engineering Procedure
ISBN 978-0-7277-6069-2

Chapter 7
Planning and control of construction

Responsibilities

The main contractor is ordinarily responsible for the planning, programming and scheduling of construction activities and, increasingly, design elements of a project. Decisions on project strategy (procurement) will impact on when the contractor will initiate this process. Early contractor involvement strategies tend to require planning activities to take place simultaneously with some detailed design packages, for example. The main contractor will work closely with their supply chain in the planning, programming and scheduling of these activities in an informal manner through existing relationships or in a formal manner, such as a preconstruction services agreement.

Initiation of construction

Starting date

In most contracts the promoter (or their representative) notifies the main contractor of the start date in writing. The contractor is then responsible for proceeding with the appropriate due diligence and, ultimately, for executing the project in accordance with the contract. Additionally, the CDM Regulations 2015 place a duty on the promoter to ensure that the main contractor does not start construction works until a satisfactory 'construction phase plan' has been submitted. The plan is an important aspect of ensuring that a culture of 'safety-centric' construction is adopted from the outset. The promoter (or their representative) should formally request the main contractor to take possession of the construction site by means of a written instruction under the contract.

Statutory notifications

Statutory planning approval for a project is usually obtained by or on behalf of the promoter. Promoters and contractors must meet legal requirements to notify new activity to statutory bodies such as the Health and Safety Executive (HSE) and local authorities.

The promoter's representative

Under the NEC3 contract, the promoter must name a person or organisation to be the project manager. Under the Infrastructure Conditions of Contract (ICC) this is the Engineer and under JCT contracts, it is the employer's representative. The person appointed then has duties and powers to administer the contract as appropriate.

The representative in administering a contract must act impartially where the contract requires him to decide any matter based on the terms of the contract. Any restrictions imposed by the promoter on the representative's authority to exercise their powers stated in a contract must be notified to prospective contractors when inviting tenders, or negotiated between promoter and contractor during the contract as a change to its terms.

When supervising the work to see that the contractor has executed their work in accordance with the contract, the representative is also the agent of the promoter, thereby acting in a dual capacity. The representative normally reports to the promoter monthly, including a review of the progress of the project, major decisions and impending important events.

In some forms of contract, the contractor will deal directly with the promoter, who will appoint members of their team to act as the representative under the contract and liaise with the contractor and will ensure that the contractor is fulfilling their obligations.

Programme and methods of construction

The construction programme is an important document. Its primary purpose is to assist the construction team with planning activities and action sequences, reporting and monitoring progress and to identify when and where additional resources may be required at key points during the construction phase. The programme document is critical to the successful execution of projects procured under NEC3; this is reflected in the 'programme clauses' which occupy a major section of the overall contract document.

Under the NEC3 conditions, the promoter's representative is required to approve the programme of construction and consent to the methods that the contractor proposes to use. The contractor must provide these under the contract if requested by the project manager. This is called the contract programme, against which the progress of the project is monitored. The programme is essential under NEC3 contracts; the ICC requires that a programme shall be submitted within 14 days of the award of the contract with a critical path network and a description of the contractors arrangements. The programme submitted for acceptance by the project manager (two weeks under the terms of NEC3) should include (Hide, 2011):

- *Key dates* – these require the contractor to meet certain conditions or complete certain tasks at given points during the execution of the contract. Where the contractor fails to meet the conditions, they become liable for any additional costs incurred by the promoter.
- *Completion date* – a fixed milestone which cannot be moved save for programme acceleration (brings date forward) or compensation events (move date back).
- *Planned completion* – does not have any impact upon the completion date; it is the date at which the contractor expects the final task on the programme to be achieved.

■ *Order and timing* – is usually a bar chart (known in project management as a Gantt chart), critical-path diagram or other software-based tool that describes the sequences of tasks, the dependencies and interdependencies, the start and finish times and float.

■ *Float* – provides an indication of the activities that can 'slip' (that is, where there is some degree of flexibility in when the activity can be completed) without adverse effect on the overall programme. In so far as NEC3 is concerned, there are three different types of float:

– *Total float* – usually calculated automatically in the programme software (although it can of course be calculated manually through the determination of the 'critical path'). The critical path is the sequence of activities in a project that, upon calculation, lead to the longest overall duration and therefore the shortest time possible to complete the project.

– *Time risk allowance* – NEC3 requires the contractor to state the elements of risk that they have applied to the determination of a given activity duration. It is usually the case that the critical-path activities will incorporate some degree of time risk allowance to provide some reassurances to the project manager that the programme (and thus the completion date) is realistic.

– *Terminal float* – the difference between the 'planned completion' and the 'completion date'.

The ownership of float can often be a contentious issue; particularly in the case of 'total float' which is, in theory, shared under NEC3 (that is, it is available to absorb the effects of compensation events or programme delay). 'Time risk allowance' and 'terminal float' are 'owned' by the contractor.

■ *Health and safety requirements* – the contractor is required to demonstrate in the programme that appropriate health and safety provisions have been included and, in particular, where specific hazards arise from any unusual activities.

■ For each operation, a statement of how the contractors plans to do the work, identifying the principal equipment and other resources which they plan to use.

■ *Dates when, in order to provide the works, the contractor will need access, plant/ materials, acceptances and so on* – this section of the programme submitted should expand on any promoter or third party interfaces – that have the ability to affect the contractor's works.

■ *Other information required in the works information* – the 'devil in the detail'; it is often the case that specific additional conditions related to the project must be considered in the programme.

Supervision

The observation and supervision of the works is undertaken by the 'supervisor' under NEC3. This representative must look ahead and discuss future parts of the project with the contractor's manager in charge at the site to ensure that they are planned to achieve the approved programme. (*Agent* was the traditional title in the UK for the contractor's representative and manager in charge on site. However, the title project manager or project director is now commonly used by contractors. These titles are not used in this guide to avoid confusion with the promoter's project manager.)

Changes, variations and compensation events

The inherent risks and uncertainties associated with civil engineering works require some degree of flexibility in the contract to allow a degree of variation to the works where it is desirable to do so. Figure 1.2 indicates that changes to design during construction can be expensive, because of the direct costs of repeating work and wasted materials, and the indirect costs associated with schedule variation. In the traditional procurement system, the promoter should not propose a change to the contractor directly. It should be discussed with the project manager and its benefits evaluated on the basis of the value to be obtained through the variation. If the promoter then wishes to make the change, the representative may be able to instruct the contractor to proceed with it, depending on the terms of the contract, or may have to negotiate it with the contractor. In NEC3 these events are referred to as 'compensation events'.

It is a contractual requirement that all variations and changes are recorded and agreed as works progress. The effect of these changes may be considered detrimental to the progress of the works and commonly form the basis of a claim.

Depending on the terms of the contract, variations may include instructions to add or omit work or change the contract programme. The project manager should then instruct the contractor by means of a formal project management instruction (PMI). The project manager should advise the promoter on variations found necessary or desirable and inform the promoter of their effects on the programme and the cost of the project.

PMIs should specify the varied work in detail. The prices to be paid for new or additional work and other effects of a variation should be stated in a PMI, if the representative has the power in the contract to do so, and if not, negotiated with the contractor. PMIs may be prepared by the representative's staff, but may be signed by them only if empowered to do so. In traditional remeasurement contracts the drawings form part of the contract. The works are remeasured in accordance with the rules of measurement and the work shown on the drawings. Any increase in quantity is not considered to be a variation unless the work shown on the drawings has changed in which case there is a variation although a 'variation order' is not required as this is essentially contained in the drawing itself.

Changes proposed by the contractor

A change proposed by the contractor must be considered by the representative and a recommendation whether or not to accept it made to the promoter. If the proposal is accepted, the representative makes it a variation ordered under the contract. In some contracts the contractor has a duty to propose variations, which they consider may be necessary for the satisfactory completion of the project. Although variations proposed by the contractor are not usually considered to be variations, care must be taken to investigate the circumstances surrounding the change request. The representative makes clear where such proposals are not considered a variation on a case-by-case basis.

Changes negotiated between promoter and contractor

The parties to a contract can agree changes to it at any time, separately from powers that the representative may have to order variations. This is necessary for a change which, for instance, the representative is not authorised by the contract to order as a variation. When such changes are agreed, the representative shall be responsible for the formal instructing of such changes in line with contract procedure.

Completion certificates

When, in their opinion, the project has been substantially completed and passed the relevant tests, the representative under the contract is required to issue a certificate to that effect. The defects correction period then normally begins.

A completion certificate may also be issued for a completed part of the project. If requested by the contractor, the representative must issue a completion certificate for a substantial part of the project if it is completed to the representative's satisfaction and is being used or occupied by the promoter or anyone acting on their behalf or under their authority.

The project must be handed over to the promoter at the end of the defects correction period in the condition required by the contract. The contractor must complete any outstanding work and also make good any defects during the defects correction period or immediately thereafter.

If any defects for which the contractor is responsible are not corrected in this period, the promoter is entitled to withhold from the balance of the retention money due to the contractor the estimated cost of such work until the contractor has completed it. Failing this, the promoter may arrange for it to be completed by others at the contractor's expense.

Responsibilities of the contractor

The responsibilities of a contractor depend upon the terms of a contract and the relevant legal jurisdiction. The following notes are written on the basis that one main contractor is 'the contractor' in control of the site, but they also apply to each of several contractors if they are working on a project in parallel.

Implementation of the works

The contractor is responsible for constructing and maintaining the project in accordance with the contract drawings, specification and other documents, and also further information and instructions issued in accordance with the contract. The contractor should be as free as possible to plan and execute the works in the way they wish within the terms of the contract. So should sub-contractors. Any requirements for part of a project to be finished before the rest and all limits to the contractor's freedom will be stated in the tender documents.

Sub-contractors may have varying status within the contract. They can be directly employed by the contractor or may be nominated by the promoter or their representative under the contract. These will be under the direct control of the main contractor. The promotor may appoint other contractors with their activities coordinated by the one principal contractor.

Health and safety

The CDM Regulations 2015 require the promoter (the regulations refer to 'client') to 'give notice in writing' to the Health and Safety Executive that construction works are to commence on site (Regulation 6). The principal designer and the principal contractor should coordinate before construction starts to review the proposed methods of construction to identify hazards, assess these and minimise their dangers to operatives on site, as well as to those who may also be affected by the works, especially the general public. In NEC3, the principal contractor is required to provide an 'activity schedule' – this is a list of activities prepared by the principal contractor which they expect to carry out in providing the works. This should form the basis of a more detailed 'constructability report' that provides information on the assessment of the various options for construction and how health and safety considerations have been considered, in consultation with the principal contractor.

Representatives of all parties on a site should attend, and meet regularly to consider health and safety needs, plan preventative measures, arrange training, and hear reports and recommendations on any accidents and near misses. Feedback should also be received from regular safety inspections and tours, with particular reference to any developing patterns.

Successive contractors may need to be named as the principal contractor if possession of the site passes from one to another. On a multi-contract site the promoter has to name one contractor as principal contractor to supervise health and safety over the whole site. Where the principal contractor has adjoining construction contracts or works with adjoining/neighbouring main contractors it is best practice to detail by way of a site plan who has principal contractor duties in which of the demarked areas of the site. In some cases this plan may be issued to a relevant statutory authority, in the UK this would be the Health and Safety Executive.

Insurance

In most contracts the contractor must insure the project until it is handed over to the promoter. The cover is usually in the joint names of the promoter and the contractor. It is, however, increasingly common for the insurance of the works to be held by the promoter, when more advantageous terms can be negotiated. Where insurance is held by the promoter it remains the responsibility of the principal contractor to notify the representative when works commence on site and of any pertinent conditions of the site or site equipment that the insurer should be made aware of.

Construction planning and control

Before the start of construction a scheme of work should be planned by the contractor's senior staff, who will be directly responsible for its execution. Decisions should be made on construction methods, site layout, temporary works, plant and the like, and requirements for labour, materials and transport. The layout of temporary works areas, buildings, offices, accommodation, stores, workshops and temporary roads and railways needs attention, because the location of these features in relation to the project can greatly affect the convenience and economy of future construction and administration. In the UK, it is also increasingly common, often under Section 106 of the Town and Country Planning Act 1990, for such matters to be explained by way of construction management plans and submitted to the local planning authority to discharge any such conditions.

Depending on the type of contract the programme produced by the contractor for tendering purposes can be either a detailed plan or an outline. In the case of a tender under the ICC contract where there is a requirement that the contractor shall submit its programme within 14 days of the award the tender programme is likely to be comprehensive as the work has been designed and there is a bill of quantities. In an NEC3 target cost where the programme has not been submitted with the tender then detailed planning is normally needed at the start of construction in order to decide how to use labour, plant, materials, finance and sub-contractors economically and safely.

As noted earlier, one of the first contractual duties of the contractor is to submit a programme for approval by the promoter's representative under the contract (although this does vary from contract to contract). This programme should show the periods for all sections of the project so that the representative can be satisfied that everything can be completed by the date specified in the contract. The contractor is also required to submit a general description of the proposed method of work. If required by the representative, this must be amended by the contractor and resubmitted at the earliest possible date.

The programme should show the promoter's representative when any further information, drawings or instructions will be required, and the dates when various sections of the project will be completed and ready for use or for the installation of equipment by other contractors. All staff on site should review the programme and progress regularly to look ahead to check that the project will be completed to the date specified in the contract.

Methods of programming

The most widely used forms of programme are bar charts and network diagrams. In its simplest form a bar chart shows a series of work activities that are simply linked as finish and start items. If a simple bar chart is the only means of analysis it provides a method of comparing planned progress with actual progress. It does not lend itself to complicated analysis of delays. However, the bar chart may have been produced from a network diagram. Network diagrams show the sequence and interdependence of activities and indicate the effects of delays. Networks may be drawn as an arrow diagram or a precedence network. Either can be used to calculate the critical path of activities, which determines the total time to complete all the work. Modern software is particularly sophisticated. This allows for programmes and charts to be shown in alternative modes, such as bar charts, networks and time-location charts.

It should also be noted that plans can now be resourced to a high degree of detail and that many uses can now be made of this data. For example, the fully resourced contract programme is increasingly becoming a tool for use by the commercial team.

Many software packages are available for displaying the network and the critical path of activities for large and complex projects. They can be used to analyse the use of resources, review progress and forecast the effects of changes in the timing of work or the use of resources. The choice of software should be made after considering how far to integrate time and cost data for planning and control and also the need to feed back the resulting data into a database for planning and costing future contracts.

Programmes

Depending upon the duration of the contract, consideration should be given to the type of programme or plan and the amount of detail contained therein. For example, a project of approximately 2 years duration would benefit from long-, medium- and short-term plans.

The long-term or overall contract programme will reflect the project requirements and will be used to pick up major items such as sub-contractors and strategic and long call-off procurement items. This plan will cover the whole duration of the project and usually will be the one that the contractor will supply to the project manager for agreement. The form of this programme can vary and may be a bar chart or a time/location chart, if the project under consideration is a linear construction, such as a highway.

A medium-term plan, which would traditionally be called the 13-week, 3-month or 100-day plan, is particularly useful for ensuring that materials are called-off in time and notices are given to sub-contractors on a timely basis. This plan will support the overall, long-term plan and will be used to progress the works accordingly. A weekly plan, which could be a 2- to 4-week rolling plan, is used to ensure that every last detail is in place for current construction. It will include details such as supervisors' names, items of plant and detailed materials quantities. All of these are supported by method statements and other project-specific documents such as the construction phase plan.

Since most planning packages are computer based, all three of the programmes can be taken as a section or slice of an overall plan. This has the advantage of being a single plan which can be updated as required.

Detailed programmes

Every section of the project should have its detailed programme to ensure that the work is planned and that methods and needs for materials are agreed in good time. Programmes should be limited in size to avoid confusion and to assist communication and understanding. Most planning software can produce critical-path diagrams and other results of data for 10 000 or so activities. To be able to understand the results it is usual to show no more than 50 activities in one programme, and to display the results in the form of a project programme. For all projects, except small ones, the use of a hierarchy of programmes is therefore recommended, with one activity in a high-level programme summarising detail shown in a lower-level programme.

Resource levelling

The contractor will normally subject the draft programmes to a 'resource levelling' study to minimise the costs of peaks and gaps of the use of plant and labour. Software programs are particularly useful for resource scheduling.

Labour planning

Contractors' estimates of the costs of work prepared for tendering are usually based on labour productivity for each type of work. These and the planned rate of work provide a basis for estimating the total labour. A chart of labour requirements can then be produced, showing by categories (skilled trades and labourers) the total numbers expected to be required at any particular time.

Economy in the use of plant and labour is achieved by planning to use it continuously and to maximum capacity. Planning and control should be in sufficient detail to see that expensive plant will not be idle for the want of adequate manpower or of transport of materials to or from the plant.

Plant planning

The construction plant that will be required and the periods during which it will be employed must be determined as early as possible, in conjunction with decisions on the detailed sequence of work and site layout. The time to obtain plant can be critical, depending on what plant is available from other contracts, what new plant should be purchased and what hired. For construction in many developing countries the need for supporting training and maintenance facilities has to be considered in deciding the choice of plant.

Programming the use of plant can be based on statistical data on the potential output for each machine and assessing the risks of interference and changes. As the work proceeds, data on actual output achieved with each major machine or set of machines should be analysed. The causes of poor output should be found, remedied and a new forecast made of when the work will be completed. Records of output achieved should also form the basis of statistics for planning future work.

Another type of planning document is the time/chainage or time/location chart. This is used to ensure that the correct sequence and logistics are in place and are useful for linear projects, such as motorways, railways and tunnelling, and for smaller jobs which are logistically challenging.

Materials planning

Materials can typically account for anywhere between 30% and 60% of the cost of construction. Their purchasing and use therefore need to be planned and controlled accurately; starting with detailed programmes which should enable buyers to draw up a schedule of materials required and ensure deliveries on time. Materials planning is now often carried out with the assistance of specialist procurement departments. When planning which materials to use, designers and contractors must give consideration to waste and resource reduction, which have become increasingly important in recent years. The decisions they make at this early stage will have an impact on the approach that will be adopted by contractors later in the process. Many promotors are keen to show that their projects will be as sustainable as possible and are setting targets for waste reduction and reuse in their construction contracts.

Sub-contracting planning

Sub-contractors should be appointed well in advance and their programmes obtained to show that they can perform their work properly and safely at, and within, the programmed time allowed. The main contractor should develop a procurement strategy and schedule detailing how each sub-contract shall be procured and the time frames for the various stages of its procurement. This schedule should be linked to the construction programme, and it should also serve as a basis on which tender information and construction issue information are released.

Integrated planning

For larger projects, with complex contractor interfaces, an integrated programme may have to be assembled to ensure that all interfaces are managed successfully. This will not change the responsibility of the contractor for their programme.

Modifications to programme

Approval of a programme does not mean that it cannot be changed, most (if not all) contracts anticipate that variations to the work will happen and a programme is used to examine the effects of any variations. A good programme is flexible enough to permit modifications to meet the more probable risks. Experience shows that a programme which allows for contingencies enables those in charge of the work to see what the effect of adverse events will be on subsequent work and adjust their plans accordingly. The working programme should therefore be updated regularly. Depending on the type of contract, the contractor should then submit a modified programme for approval by the promoter's representative.

Design of temporary works

The contractor is usually responsible for the design of the temporary works it proposes to use, but these are of course subject to legal requirements for health and safety and specific regulations for independent checking of major falsework and other temporary structures, such as British Standards. The contractor will usually formally appoint a member of the construction delivery team to hold the legal duties of a 'temporary works coordinator'.

The contractor is required to submit drawings and design calculations for temporary works to the project manager; these should be scrutinised with care. This does not relieve the contractor of its responsibility for the design and construction of the temporary works, but it should reduce the risk of mistakes and assists the project manager in discharging their responsibility to the promoter to see that the work is done satisfactorily and safely. Depending upon the assessment of the risk of the temporary works, the contractor and/or sub-contractor may be required to have such drawings and calculations prepared or checked by an independent engineer. Useful information on the design of temporary works can be sourced from the 'Temporary Works Forum' www.twforum. org.uk.

Quality

Contracts usually specify in detail the quality of materials and workmanship required, and the tests required to prove compliance. When planning the construction work the contractor should make sure that the proposed methods and plant can produce work to the quality specified. During the work the contractor's senior management have to ensure that quality is achieved. Most contractors have quality assurance systems that are designed to ensure this for all their work, and will in many cases produce a site-specific quality plan, which may be included in the overall health, safety quality and environment management plan. It is also best practice for the contractor to prepare and submit to the representative, package and work-specific inspection and test plans (ITPs) detailing on- and off-site quality assurance compliance checking.

Setting out

The contractor is usually responsible for setting out the works. The promoter's representative or assistants normally check the setting out in order to minimise the risk of errors and consequent delays to progress. If the setting out is particularly complex, a specialist sub-contractor may be employed by the contractor.

Reporting

The contractor is normally required to report on a regular basis on the progress and quality of construction and the supporting activities of ordering materials and designing temporary works. 'Returns' (data) of the number and classes of labour and plant employed on site by the contractor and sub-contractors are usually also required, together with reports on any accidents and near misses. The representative should agree with the principal contractor the expected content of all progress reports and the frequency that they are to be issued.

Progress

Statements of elapsed time, labour hours or money expended are of little use on their own, because they give no indication of what has been produced and when things will be completed. Data on progress should therefore be compared with predictions and the programmes to provide the basis for any action needed to achieve completion dates in a timely manner. A convenient way of expressing progress is by using indices. Commonly, a schedule index and a commercial index are produced. These are generally functions of 'earned value'. The programme will typically show a planned duration of the works. By comparing the actual performance of construction with planned performance values can be attributed to the actual and earned durations. Hence, useful indices can be calculated for use when analysing and predicting performance. Common techniques used for progress monitoring of civil engineering projects include (APM, 2013):

- *Earned value management* – a project control process based on a structured approach to planning, cost collection and performance measurement. It facilitates the integration of project scope, time and cost objectives and the establishment of a baseline plan of performance measurement.
- *S-curves* – a simple graphical representation of cumulative costs, labour hours or other quantities (y-axis), plotted against time (x-axis).

- *Line of balance technique* – a scheduling technique for delivery of repetitive products that shows how resource teams move from product to product rather than the detail of individual activities.
- *Critical-chain method* – a networking technique that identifies paths through a project based on resource dependencies, as well as technical dependencies.

Cash flow

Every contractor and sub-contractor that is due to be paid according to progress of work needs to plan their expected cash flow when tendering, and then to monitor it during the work. Earlier expenditure or later payment than expected can incur greater costs for a contractor, which can impact severely on expected profit.

In 2008, the UK Office for Government Commerce (now Cabinet Office) issued guidance on improving payment practices in public sector projects. This was designed to address a widespread concern that contractors and suppliers were increasingly bedevilled by late payments for completed work. The recommendations are:

- The adoption of a '*Fair Payment Charter*' on each and every project. This is essentially a non-binding agreement between the promoter and the main contactor (and the supply chain).
- The adoption of '*fair payment practices*', including the use of milestone payments, payment schedules, 'open book' accounting and 30-day payment cycles.
- The use of '*project bank accounts*', which have trust status and only allow outgoing payments to the contractor and the supply-chain participants.

It is also worth noting that the treatment of payments and cash flows in NEC3 is different to those in, for example, JCT11.

Cost monitoring systems

It is good practice on all jobs for every contractor and sub-contractor should have a site cost recording and monitoring system that provides:

- accurate reports at regular intervals of the unit costs of all the principal work and overhead charges
- estimates of the likely final costs
- data in the form required for claiming progress payments
- cost data of the completed works to guide future estimating.

The data are needed whether the contract is fixed priced or costs are reimbursable. They are confidential to each contractor and sub-contractor unless required for payments under a reimbursable contract or part of a contract.

Labour and plant costs depend mainly on good planning, control and discipline on site. All these costs should be recorded, reported and analysed, usually weekly, to ascertain whether these resources were used productively, so that remedial action on problems can be taken before large wasteful costs have been incurred.

Material costs are monitored to see whether materials are being used economically and to identify and remedy cases of waste and other losses. The accuracy of a costing system is very dependent on information from foremen, gangers, machine drivers and other operators on how labour hours have been used. The definitions of cost items should therefore be clear to them. Where a bill of quantities has been provided the bill items will need to be divided into its elemental cost for analysis purposes.

Each contractor and sub-contractor also needs an internal accounts system, which provides reports and forecasts of expenditure, commitments, liabilities, cash flow and the expected final financial state of their contract. Some or most of the cost monitoring and accounting required may be provided by a regional office or the company head office.

Payment to contractor and sub-contractors
Monthly statements for interim certificates
In most civil engineering contracts the contractor is entitled to monthly payments for work completed. A statement (application) showing the amount due during the month in question is prepared and submitted by the contractor in a form usually specified by the contract. This is usually prepared by a contractor's quantity surveyor (CQS) and will be evaluated by the promoter's quantity surveyor (often referred to as a PQS).

The statement should be checked and agreed by the promoter's representative who will, after verification, send to the promoter a certificate showing the amount to be paid to the contractor. On receipt of this certificate, the contractor will submit an invoice for payment within the agreed time frame.

In a traditional remeasurement contract, payment for the work done is based on the contractor's tender rates for each item listed in the bill of quantities. Alternatively, the terms of the contract may be that payment is due when the contractor completes defined stages of work (milestones). This basis of payment is becoming more common, as it is directly related to progress towards the promoter's objectives.

In cost-reimbursable contracts, payment may depend upon agreement of the value of progress achieved, not simply the costs incurred. In most contracts the promoter is obliged to pay the contractor within a specified period.

Some contracts allow for neutral cash flow, which means that the contractor will be given some form of advanced payment based on a forecast of expenditure.

Final payment

The final balance of payment is usually due to the contractor at the end of the defect correction period (this is the rectification period in JCT11 contracts). By then the promoter's representative should expect a final account from the contractor and be preparing to check it and issue the final certificate. If there remain outstanding claims from the contractor, these should be settled under the procedure stated in the contract.

Claims and disputes

The procedure to be followed in the settlement of any claims and disputes that may arise during the execution of the contract is ordinarily established in the conditions of contract. Where claims/disputes arise under the NEC3 (ECC, Professional Services Contract and Term Service Contract), the first stage is mediation. By way of the 'escalation' procedures written into the contract, in the situation where mediation fails the next stage is adjudication. If the claim/dispute remains unresolved, then arbitration or litigation should follow. NEC3 sets out two options: W1 and W2. These reflect the requirement for alternative dispute resolution (ADR) procedures in the UK under the Local Democracy, Economic Development and Construction Act 2009, instead of immediate recourse to adjudication, arbitration or litigation. ADR is based on the use of neutral experts attempting to resolve the dispute in a collaborative manner; the use of ADR will require the parties to move from a combative into a collaborative role working together towards a solution that both can accept.

Communications and records

Communications between the promoter's representative under the contract and the contractor should be in writing, or confirmed in writing. Every document exchanged between the contractor and the promoter or their representative on the execution of the project – all emails, letters, memos, drawings, sketches, photographs, minutes of meetings, progress and other reports, monthly measurements, claims and certificates – becomes part of the administration of the contract, unless agreed otherwise. All these and physical records of site conditions should be kept and filed to form the contract records.

Documents whose importance or usefulness is not wholly clear at the time may become so later, for instance to help with such things as analysing the causes of accidents, failures or deterioration of completed work, the state of buried work, disagreements between the promoter's representative and the contractor over payments or delays, and designing and pricing additional work. The records that should be kept include:

- diaries – most importantly, every engineer on a contract should keep a detailed diary of their own work, however insignificant the detail may seem at the time
- notes of oral instructions or agreements

- superseded drawings, which must be kept because something done when the drawing was current may seem very odd several years (and numerous revisions) later
- an up-to-date health and safety file (a requirement under the CDM Regulations 2015), to guide all who will work on any future design, construction, maintenance or demolition of the project, and records of safety training and meetings
- as-built drawings – in practice the need to break into old work often reveals that the record drawings are out-of-date or incomplete
- photographs detailing the progress of the works at regular intervals.

FURTHER READING AND REFERENCES

APM (Association for Project Management) (2013) *Body of Knowledge*, 6th edn. Princes Risborough, UK.

Barnes PT, Farren R, Haidar AD and Wells KP (2015) *Programme Management in Construction*. ICE Publishing, London.

NEC3: Introduction to the ECC (2013) Course Notes L06301.

Hide G (2011) *ECC Clause 31.2 – Programme Requirements*. http://gmhplanning.co.uk/nec3-guidance-notes/ecc-clause-31-2-programme-requirements/ (accessed 19 August 2015).

Neale D, Neale RH and Stephenson P (2016) *Construction Planning*, 2nd edn. ICE Publishing, London, UK.

Sheridan P and Marvin J (2010) *NEC3 Dispute Resolution Provisions*. http://www.sheridangold.co.uk/assets/depot/files/d001_nec3_dispute_provisions_article_sg.pdf (accessed 19 August 2015).

Civil Engineering Procedure
ISBN 978-0-7277-6069-2

Chapter 8
Construction management organisation

Size and organisation

Developments in procurement and contracts coupled with diversification of many traditional contracting businesses has led to a myriad of organisation designs. Most tend to adopt 'variations on a theme' and in this chapter we consider traditional and early contractor involvement (ECI) organisational strategies, where there is one principal contractor. Whilst the following primarily considers the NEC suite of contracts the comments and discussions are equally valid for the efficient management of any construction project. The role of the various professionals responsible for the delivery of the project has become much more complex with commercial and contractual matters being increasingly important with more work being sub-contracted. Risk identification and management is now a major part of the site team's workload for both the promoter's staff and the contractor's.

The promoter's representative

Traditionally in civil engineering projects in the UK, the consulting engineer acted as the representative of the promoter (in the ICE 7th edition Conditions of Contact); the Engineer is maintained in the ICC but has changed to the project manager in the NEC. Today, NEC3 is widely used and this has led to the advent of the project management professional.

Consultant's project manager

The term project manager or design project manager is commonly used within consultancy organisations for the project engineer with responsibility for the following:

- to plan and supervise detailed design, if not already complete, and coordinate the issue of any further drawings to the contractor under whatever procedure is stated in the contract
- to promote and implement value engineering and innovative ideas
- to direct redesign if there are varied requirements of the promoter or changed site conditions

- to estimate the effect that any variations will have on the programme and cost of the project, and to advise on issuing a promoter's change/project manager's instruction or whatever procedure is stated in the contract
- to advise the promoter on the progress, trends and likely outcome of contracts
- to manage the project risks
- to manage third party customer care
- to actively manage environmental risks
- to promote a partnering ethos to engender mutual trust and cooperation
- to administer the issue of the certificates for payment to the contractor
- to advise the promoter on compensation events, claims and disputes
- to liaise with the supervisor/promoter's representative on all the above.

Under the NEC3 form of contract, the 'project manager' is named within the contract and is appointed by the promoter to manage the contract on their behalf. The contractual role of the project manager is defined in terms of the decisions and actions they have to take.

Delegation of authority

Under the NEC3 form of contract, the responsibility for most communications with the contractor is usually delegated to the supervisor by the project manager. The extent to which the project manager can delegate their powers is usually limited in the contract. The project manager should inform the contractor in writing of the extent of delegation of their powers.

The supervisor

The role of the supervisor under NEC3 is to check that the project is constructed in accordance with the contract. The principal duties are:

- to carry out the duties delegated by the project manager
- to check that the contractor has organised their work to achieve the accepted or approved programme
- to examine the methods proposed by the contractor for the execution of the project, the primary object being to see that they should ensure safe and satisfactory construction
- to ensure that the contractor complies with the requirements of the project health and safety plan
- to assist the contractor to interpret drawings and understand the specification, and refer questions to the design project manager/project engineer
- to supervise the project to ensure that it is being executed in line with the requirements of the project quality plan
- to assess and record the progress of the work in comparison with the programme

- to execute and/or supervise tests carried out on the site, and inspect materials and manufacture at source
- to keep a diary constituting a detailed history of the work done and all events at the site and submit periodic progress reports to the project manager
- to advise the project manager on the monthly assessments of the amount due to the contractor
- to agree and record the relevant facts for any work or event for which the contractor may claim additional time or payment
- to direct the production of as-built drawings and the health and safety file
- to manage risk by advising the project manager on potential problems in good time for them to be avoided or their effects minimised.

The supervisor's site team

Save for small projects, the supervisor usually leads a team of assistant engineers, inspectors and support staff. Their actual numbers and organisation depend upon the size of the project, the complexity of work and distance from head office or services.

The role of the inspectors is to supervise the contractor's work, for instance the mixing and placing of concrete and any such work requiring constant supervision. The duties of inspectors demand practical experience, objectivity and tact in order to gain the respect of the foremen and skilled workers employed by the contractor. Corresponding roles are needed in other contract arrangements, for instance where a project is designed and supervised by the promoter's own staff.

Early contractor involvement

The promoter's representative role is determined by the type of contract and the stage at which a contractor is engaged to take responsibility for the project development (early engagement is more commonly known by the acronym (ECI). Until the contractor is procured, the promoter's representative responsibilities cover the following:

- develop the design within the required scope and brief, ensuring compliance with CDM Regulations 2015
- manage the scheme development through the planning or statutory processes
- achieve a satisfactory outcome at any public inquiry if required
- assist the promoter to define the budgets and programme requirements
- manage consultations with stakeholders, the public and other interested parties
- ensure there is effective communication between the contractor and the promoter.

The promoter may wish to procure the contractor early, at which point some of the responsibilities above may be transferred to the contractor. These will be determined within the contract.

During construction, the role of the promoter's representative is greatly reduced from the role previously outlined for 'construct only' schemes. Their main responsibility is to monitor the following:

■ the progress of the contractor and keep the promoter fully informed
■ deal with scheme changes and events on behalf of the promoter
■ determine the payments to be made to the contractor based on work completed.

Main contractor's organisation

Figure 8.1 provides a basic framework outline of a contractor's structure of company departments and the main responsibilities for managing contracts. All roles under the operational and commercial directors are responsible for project delivery. However,

Figure 8.1 Organogram showing example organisational structure of a construction contracting organisation

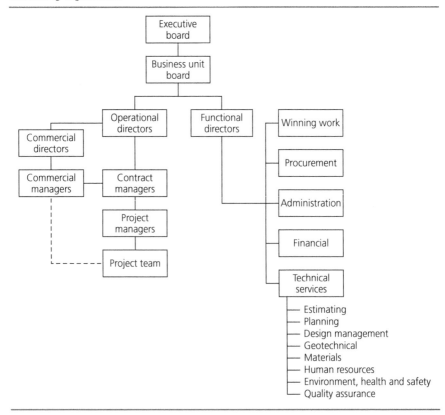

these teams are supported by functions that are located off-site in the company's head office or a regional office.

Although all projects are different a typical site management structure for work involving building façade and fit out work might be as shown in Figure 8.2. Here some roles are specialist ones in a function or discipline, for instance planning. Others are in a section or area of the site. The nature of these duties varies significantly, depending on the variety of work, size and layout of a site and the terms of the contract. On major projects there tend to be more specialists; on smaller and traditional contracts there tends to be a wider range of responsibilities for each individual.

Contractors' project managers and agents

Contractors' project managers are usually experienced engineers. Most of the financial risks of a traditional construction contract are on site and so the contractor's project manager is usually given wide powers by their company to plan and control the work. The project manager's main role is to successfully deliver the scheme to time, cost and budget, which includes responsibilities for the following:

- construction
- health, safety and environment
- compliance with the contract
- the commercial success of the contract
- management of the contractor's site staff
- programme management
- liaison with the supervisor
- stakeholder liaison and communication
- risk management
- performance management
- advising the promoter on scheme budgets.

Sub-agents, package managers and construction managers

On larger sites, areas of the work are usually the responsibility of sub-agents (increasingly known as package managers and construction managers). Depending on the size of the particular project, they will have varying numbers of staff, principally section engineers, assistant engineers and inspectors. Sub-agents' main responsibilities are:

- day-to-day site management
- health and safety
- industrial relations
- management of sub-contractors
- productivity and workmanship of the plant and labour.

Figure 8.2 Organogram showing example construction project management structure

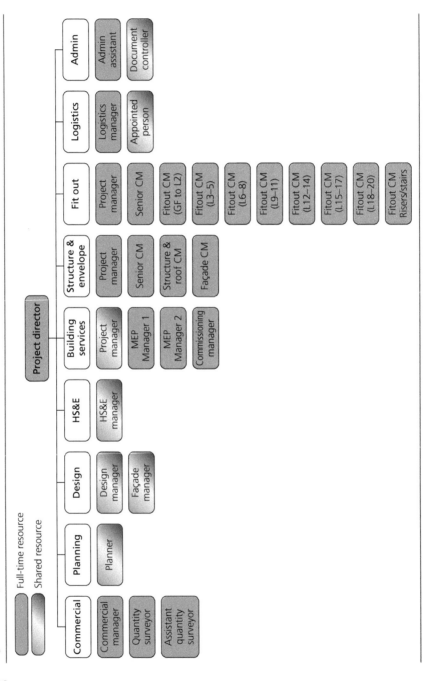

The general foreman and sectional foremen, depending on the size, variety and spread of work, usually supervise the use of labour, plant and transport.

General foreman

The general foreman is the link between the management and the foremen and gangers in direct charge of labour. Their personal influence on the site organisation can be a strong factor in achieving and maintaining efficiency. Sub-contractors increasingly provide the role, more so than main contractors.

The general foreman's main responsibilities are:

- allocation of labour to site operations
- supervising flows of materials and the management of stores/compound areas
- motivation of the labour force
- site communications between all foremen and gangers
- site safety – including workforce briefings, statutory inspections and site tidiness.

Principal engineer/engineering manager (on large projects)

The chief engineer is responsible for the technical methods needed to ensure the quality and accuracy of the works, through guidance of the section engineers and all the contractor's staff. They are responsible for any design needed on site, especially of temporary works, and will draw on head office engineering and research departments where appropriate.

Section engineers

Section engineers usually have an appreciation of design, construction, health, safety and environmental requirements. They are ultimately responsible to the project manager/agent, but are usually directed by the sub-agent. On large or technically complex schemes they will obtain assistance and technical guidance from the chief engineer. They report progress and measurement/scheme change issues to the quantity surveyor. Each section engineer must liaise with the foreman in his or her section, to plan the work to be executed daily, weekly and monthly.

Contractor's quantity surveyor (CQS) or cost engineer

On larger projects, a quantity surveyor or cost engineer (modern parlance describes the role as 'commercial management') and assistants may be needed to record the quantities of work done, manage sub-contractors' payments and prepare the information for the contractor to request payment as defined under the contract. Interim and final measurements have to be substantiated and agreed with the supervisor.

The quantity surveyor will notify the supervisor of any events or changes in work scope and they will be responsible for evaluating and agreeing the effect of change. If agreement of these variations is not achieved, the quantity surveyor will assist in the dispute resolution procedure defined in the contract.

Normally, the quantity surveyor is also responsible for managing correspondence and instructions on the main contract and sub-contracts, and advising the contractor's project manager/agent on contract and sub-contract matters. On smaller projects these tasks are part of the job of sub-agents or section engineers, supported by a visiting quantity surveyor.

Planner/scheduler

The planner/scheduler is responsible for the development of the overall contract programme in conjunction with other key members of the project team. They will update the overall contract programme with progress to date at intervals specified in the contract or as required by the project manager. They will also usually provide the site team with a weekly or fortnightly programme giving the work elements for the forthcoming month. It will be either a full-time or part-time role, depending on the size and nature of the scheme.

Quality/safety/environmental sustainability coordinator

The role of the coordinator is to develop, manage, implement and regularly monitor the requirements of the project quality plan, health and safety plan and environmental management plan. These roles are carried out by one person or by separate individuals, depending on the size of the project. Many contractors now have an integrated management system, which combines the business processes for all these three areas.

Community and local liaison manager

For nearly all projects that require the specialist services of a public liaison officer, the duties can be described as follows:

- Consultation and liaison with affected landowners, residents and local businesses. Assisting at key liaison group meetings. Communicating back to the project team.
- Provision of a regular surgery or hold public exhibitions for the public for general discussion, raise issues and so on.
- Respond to compliments and deal with complaints.
- Control and organisation of the media, local radio, leaflet/letter drops on progress, town notice board, dedicated email address, traffic switches and so on.
- Liaison with and organisation of trips and visits by local schools and interested parties.
- Oversee and report on local labour employment requirements.
- Monitor Section 106 compliance requirements.

Logistics manager/controller
Construction projects are increasingly organised along the lines of supply-chain management principles. This requires adequate systems to manage the delivery of materials and plant in addition to other transport operations. The logistics manager will manage key interfaces with project planners, commercial managers and the construction managers on the site to ensure that the project team is fully aware of logistics in support of the construction programme.

Information manager/document controller
The advent of building information modelling (BIM) has emphasised the need for a professional role in information coordination and knowledge management. On complex projects, large volumes of digital and paper documents are produced and this can create difficulties in ensuring that information is made available to the right people, at the right time. The Construction Industry Council (CIC) BIM Protocol requires the appointment of an information manager. The main role of the information manager, according to the protocol, is to establish, monitor and manage the common data environment (CDE) and ensure that the project data follow the agreed protocol.

Support functions
Most contractors will have head office support functions as indicated on Figure 8.1. They are responsible for both support to the project and for ensuring a consistency of standards and approach across the organisation.

Appointment of site staff
If the works are to start well and proceed economically, much will depend on the early appointment of the contractor's project manager/agent and their staff so that they can begin their planning and other preparations and establish selection, induction and training facilities before labour arrives in any numbers. There is a risk that these preparations will be inadequately planned if one person has to do several others' work during the initial period.

Selection of adequate and experienced staff, and briefing them on the project, its priorities, risks and organisation, are particularly important if the site is remote – and especially if overseas (Loraine, 1991). Ideally, key members of the team should be involved with the project at bid stage to facilitate continuity, however in all cases a formal handover to the site staff should be carried out.

Industrial relations – communications and procedures
The Working Rule Agreement for the Construction Industry (Construction Industry Joint Council), negotiated between the promoters' representatives and trades unions, sets out 31 'working rules' that cover issues such as holiday entitlement, disciplinary procedures, grievance procedures and sick pay. Increasingly contractors and sub-contractors

in the UK employ skilled and other labour as individual sub-contractors rather than as permanent employees, as this is can provide greater flexibility to the promoter and can have tax advantages to the employees, but the Working Rule Agreement provides a basis for their employment. Thorough knowledge of this Agreement and the amendments made to it from time to time is required for successful industrial relations. The latest revision of the agreement took place in 2013.

Civil engineering in the UK has comparatively good industrial relations and care should be taken to maintain them. The management being seen to be consistent, fair and reasonable achieves good industrial relations on site. To this end, good communication systems are essential. Management should always be prepared to meet employees' representatives, resolve factual questions and explain policies. In the UK and Ireland, the main trade union representing construction workers is the Union of Construction, Allied Trades and Technicians (UCATT).

Suitable provisions should be made for foreign/migrant workers, particularly in the context of health, safety and welfare. There are a number of considerations including:

- language skills and competence of workers on site
- knowledge and awareness of health and safety legislation
- cultural norms
- knowledge of construction methods, plant and equipment.

Incentives

Contractors use incentive bonus schemes to try to achieve good productivity from manual employees. The basis of a good incentive scheme is that it should give a person of average ability the opportunity to earn more than their basic wage in return for increased production. It is important that it is clearly understood what is expected in terms of increased production, the normal needs to be established first and then the incentive calculated on production rates in excess of the normal rate. Incentive schemes need to be seen to be fair and require both technical and psychological skills to formulate and apply. Without adequate safeguards in place, workforce discontent can quickly arise. Weekly measurement of production and the calculation of bonuses require promptness and accuracy.

Production targets and the bonus applicable to them should be clear and agreed between a contractor or sub-contractor and the representative of their employees, and thereafter altered only if circumstances justify changes.

Not all work can be made the subject of a bonus by the direct measurement of output. Employees who provide support services to those on bonus targets should therefore be given a financial interest in the work, that attracts bonuses and so gain some benefit when bonuses are earned by their colleagues.

Site office administration

An administration/office manager (titles vary) on larger or remote sites is usually responsible for secretarial and other administrative services to the site organisation, the keeping of attendance and sickness records, minor purchasing, and the checking of the receipt and safeguarding of materials. On smaller and urban sites, the contractor's head or regional offices provide most or all of these services.

Sub-contractors' organisations

Sub-contractors' organisations are generally similar to those of main contractors, but smaller and more specialised to suit their scale and range of work. Many projects are now carried out in a partnering environment in which major sub-contractors form part of the integrated project team.

Design and build

In many circumstances the promoter employs the contractor to design and build a particular project. The extent of the contractor's design responsibilities will depend upon the point in the process at which the contractor is employed and it will be defined within the contract.

Some of the promoter's representative responsibilities outlined previously for construct only will consequently be transferred to the contractor. The contractor employs a designer to complete the design and supervision on the contractor's behalf.

Where this occurs the contractor's designer is responsible for:

- developing a buildable, cost-effective design solution within the required scope and brief
- obtaining all the necessary approvals and certification
- ensuring the design is completed within the cost and programme constraints
- developing the environmental management plan taking into account all environmental constraints
- dealing effectively and in a timely manner with scheme changes
- site supervision and auditing the contractor's site quality records
- assisting the contractor in updating the scheme budgets.

Design manager

For these schemes the contractor may employ a design manager/design coordinator to manage the interface between the contractor and their designer. Key duties include:

- providing a clear design brief
- assisting the designer with buildability, value engineering and designing out risks
- agreeing the design programme and planned resources
- regularly reviewing progress, costs to date and forecast costs with the designer
- effectively managing design change
- liaising with the site team on preferred solutions and design development.

The Considerate Constructors Scheme

The UK Considerate Constructors Scheme (CCS) has the primary function of providing guidance designed to ensure that the negative impacts of a construction project are minimised. The CCS sets out a 'Code of Considerate Practice' that commits registered sites and companies to care about appearance, respect the community, protect the environment, secure everyone's safety and value their workforce.

The Construction Skills Certification Scheme

The Construction Skills Certification Scheme (CSCS) provides certification within the UK construction industry to ensure that individuals working on construction sites have attained the required levels of training and qualification for the type of work they undertake. The scheme provides recognition of various job roles through the provision of a database of people working in the construction industry who 'have or are committed to achieving, a recognised construction related qualification'. It is now commonplace for main contractors to require workers on site to hold a valid CSCS card. This does not, however, relieve the contractor of its duty to ensure safe working practices and it should carry out regular safety compliance tests.

FURTHER READING AND REFERENCES

Bennett J (1991) *International Construction Project Management: General Theory and Practice*. Butterworth-Heinemann, Oxford, UK.

Bower D (2003) *Management of Procurement*. Thomas Telford, London, UK.

Howes R and Tah JMH (2003) *Strategic Management Applied to International Construction*. Thomas Telford, London, UK.

Levy SM (2006) *Project Management in Construction*. McGraw-Hill, New York, NY, USA.

Loftus J (1999) *Project Management of Multiple Projects and Contracts*. Thomas Telford, London, UK.

Loraine RK (1991) *Construction Management in Developing Countries*. Thomas Telford, London, UK.

Martin AS and Grover F (eds) (1998) *Managing People*. Thomas Telford, London, UK.

Morris P (1997) *The Management of Projects*. Thomas Telford, London, UK.

Civil Engineering Procedure
ISBN 978-0-7277-6069-2

ICE Publishing: All rights reserved
http://dx.doi.org/10.1680/cep.60692.113

Chapter 9
Inspection, testing, commissioning and handover

Planning and organisation

The period of inspection, testing, commissioning and handover marks an important transitional stage in a civil engineering project; it is the period during which the main construction activities conclude and the asset is prepared for operational use. For the simplest of projects, this stage may consist only of a formal handover. For more complex schemes, featuring high degrees of mechanical and electrical services, controls and equipment, this stage is usually a separate set of inspection, testing and commissioning activities, which overlap their supply and installation. Detailed considerations in respect of the exact status of the asset and its 'ownership' and so on will depend on exactly whom is being defined as the promoter and on the specific provisions of the procurement strategy and the subsequent 'utilisation' of the asset during its operational life. For example, originally the infrastructure for the Lewisham and the Woolwich extensions of the Docklands Light Railway (DLR) in London was procured under public private partnership (PPP) contracts that included their ongoing maintenance, although the DLR operations using them were the subject of a separate operating concession. Rather differently, the original Manchester Metrolink phase 1 (Altrincham–Bury) and phase 2 (Eccles) PPP contracts involved both the construction and subsequent operation, but all of the capital assets (infrastructure and trams) remained owned by the local passenger transport authority as promoter. By contrast the original Nottingham Express Transit was procured by a private finance initiative (PFI) deal in which the infrastructure and trams were fully financed, supplied and operated by the concessionaire in return for an annual facilities fee as well as any operating surplus resulting from the fares revenue and so on. In summary, this phase of the project life cycle requires an understanding of what is being 'handed-over' and to whom.

Planning

Inspection, testing, commissioning and handover requirements should be incorporated in planning activities from the earliest stages of a project, so that provision for them can be made during design and in allocating responsibilities to the principal contractor. Together with the necessary budget provisions, this planning is a key aspect of the project strategy. Suitable provisions can then be included in the relevant contracts with regard to responsibilities for inspection, testing, commissioning, partial and full hand-over, including commissioning by both the promoter and the contractor (this process can be significantly more complex if a separate 'operating contractor' or 'concessionaire' is involved). 'Taking over' arrangements may be required to enable the promoter's business/service requirements alongside construction or fit-out work within a partially operational asset.

Detailed planning of inspection, testing and commissioning activities will usually be necessary in the pre-commissioning stage, in parallel with construction.

Organisation and resources

The promoter may need to establish a commissioning and occupation team, which includes their own representatives, others who are to be the eventual owners, users or occupiers, the engineering team and specialist commissioning personnel. The resources needed should be identified and procured early in the project. An effective and active management structure should be established under the project manager, who should ensure that the responsibilities of each party are clearly defined and planned in order to ensure the smooth commissioning and handover of the project.

Health and safety

The inspection, testing, commissioning and operation of equipment and systems in a completed or partially completed asset may include hazards that are unfamiliar to the construction team. Other personnel from various organisations are likely to be working closely together, many not familiar with site hazards.

Health and safety responsibilities and the transfer of the control of hazards, through the handover of the health and safety file, from construction to commissioning and operations staff should therefore be clearly defined and effective permit-to-work and other control procedures established. Detailed studies of hazards and responsibilities, and training and induction in health and safety for all personnel during this stage are required.

Case study 5: Commissioning and testing of the Manchester Metrolink upgrade during refurbishment of Manchester Victoria railway station

Manchester Victoria station, originally opened in 1844, is a busy inter-urban railway station that had, until 2013, suffered many years of neglect. Network Rail embarked upon a £44 million redevelopment scheme in early 2013 to modernise the station. The scope of works included:

■ A new £16 million roof structure and cladding featuring ethylene tetrafluoroethylene (ETFE) pillows and rainwater harvesting system.
■ Station concourse enhancements, including a new fully accessible bridge linking the station to Manchester Arena, and to the footbridge spanning platforms 3–6.
■ New retail spaces.
■ Refurbishment of the original ticket hall with modern glazed entrances.

During the project, remodelling of the Victoria Metrolink stop (a light rail system connecting various locations within the Greater Manchester conurbation, including Salford, Bury, Rochdale and Trafford) was planned to provide additional capacity at the station and facilitate the planned Metrolink Second City Crossing expansion project. The majority of the Metrolink works involved the realignment of the Metrolink tracks into and in the station and the upgrade of the stop itself to two new island platforms. A significant challenge to the project team was created by the interface of this work within the site boundaries of the Manchester Victoria scheme. Victoria station remained operational throughout the construction programme and this introduced additional challenges, particularly in terms of testing and commissioning the Metrolink work within a live construction site and operational railway station. Usually, testing and commissioning work in light rail schemes such as Metrolink can be described in a four-stage process (Sharma, 2010):

1 Factory acceptance/inspection test (FAT) – to ensure that all components and equipment meet specifications.
2 Site installation test (SIT) – to demonstrate that all equipment is correctly installed, wired, checked and suitable for operation.
3 Site acceptance test (SAT) – the pre-commissioning phase, which is designed to show that the equipment and sub-systems can functionally operate as an integrated system.
4 Overall site acceptance/performance test (SATOV) – the commissioning stage, which is designed to demonstrate that the overall system will operate satisfactorily in commercial service and can be handed over to the promoter.

The subsequent timing and scheduling of these activities are likely to be time critical in almost all projects, but the wider Manchester Victoria redevelopment scheme introduced additional complexities for the project team. The systems involved in the testing and commissioning phase range from the 'heavy' civil engineering, such as the permanent way, overhead line equipment and gantries, signalling and platform furniture, through to the technology interfaces, such as closed-circuit television (CCTV).

The testing and commissioning phase is a multi-disciplinary effort involving the promoter, the designers, the main contractor and specialist sub-contractor, suppliers and the various statutory authorities.

The Manchester Victoria Metrolink stop was successfully completed and reopened to passengers on 18 February 2015, with anticipated completion of the whole of the Manchester Victoria station project in winter 2015.

The Manchester Victoria Metrolink stop works and associated enhancements were funded by the Greater Manchester Transport Fund and European Regional Development Fund Programme 2007–2013.

Figure 9.1 Manchester Metrolink upgrade project

Inspection and testing of work

Inspection and testing

During construction and on completion of parts of a project, inspection and testing are usually required in order to confirm compliance with the drawings and specification. Inspection and testing are generally required for static components of a project, while dynamic components such as machinery require testing and commissioning. In NEC3, the project manager, supported by their team, is usually responsible for inspections on and off site and for testing of materials.

Test criteria and schedules

The performance tests and criteria to be applied to any aspect of work should be specified in the contract for that work so as to enable the identification of the state at which an acceptable quality or degree of completion has been achieved. Depending on the type of project, samples and mock-ups or factory inspections and acceptance tests may be required. If they are, the responsibility for their cost should be defined. Schedules (lists) of the necessary inspections and tests should be agreed through collaboration between the project manager and parties to the contract.

Commissioning

Commissioning roles

Commissioning should be the orderly process of testing, adjustment and bringing the operational units of the project into use. It is generally required where systems and equipment are to be brought into service following installation. Commissioning may be carried out by the promoter's or contractor's staff, by specialist personnel or by a mixed team. For complex industrial projects, a commissioning manager is usually appointed by the promoter to plan the commissioning, preferably early in the project, establish budgets, lead a commissioning team and procure other necessary resources. For simple projects, commissioning is usually undertaken by the contractor, subject to the approval of procedures by the promoter or their representative under the contract. The commissioning of familiar or small process and industrial facilities is usually carried out by the operator (or, dependent on the contract, the contractor, the concessionaire, the promoter or the owner) with the advice and assistance of the suppliers of the equipment and systems.

Organisation and management

Whatever the contractual relationships, the commissioning and occupation of a large project can involve a number of parties and risks. Active management, clear procedures and effective communication are therefore essential. The management organisation for pre-commissioning and commissioning should be agreed, and key personnel mobilised, during the construction stage, and organised so as to provide:

- A simple structure to suit the specialised nature of the work, with clear responsibilities and without multiple layers of management.
- A single point responsibility for all commissioning activities at all times, under the direction of a commissioning manager.
- Rigorous procedures in respect of health and safety.

Commissioning process

The commissioning process may need to allow for continuing construction alongside commissioning activities and, in many cases, occupation of premises or operation of completed systems. So, while construction proceeds on the basis of physical site areas and technical specialisations, commissioning usually has to be undertaken on complete operating sub-systems and units.

Commissioning schedule

For all but simple static work, the commissioning manager should draft a schedule listing all the items to be commissioned, their interdependence and the standards of performance to be achieved. Commissioning is usually carried out progressively at the levels of sub-units, units, systems and the whole project. The schedule should provide for these activities being carried out sequentially, alongside continuing construction. Contingency plans should also be prepared, to allow alternative commissioning sequences if problems are encountered.

Commissioning plan

The commissioning plan should include a programme and identify all activities and the necessary resources and procedures. These should include the supply of power, water or other services for testing, materials, consumables, replacement items, labour and specialist expertise. Furthermore, clarity regarding the communications and notifications of any relevant regulatory/statutory authorities, who may need prior notification of commissioning activities and may need to give approval for or have the right to inspect them or resulting records. The plan should also identify procedures for managing emergencies and for rectifying defects, both before and after handover.

Staffing and training

In order to ensure that the project is put into operation rapidly, safely and effectively, all the commissioning, operating and maintenance personnel should be appointed, trained and briefed before commissioning starts. This needs to be planned from project inception, so that the roles and activities of the commissioning and operating staff are integrated into a coherent team to maximise their effectiveness.

Completion and handover

Practical and sectional completion, partial possession and taking over

In most construction contracts there is provision for sectional completion and handover of a project. This is particularly the case in transport infrastructure projects where there is a need to maintain services. Once the contractor considers they have completed the scope of work within their responsibility and has fulfilled all the necessary obligations relating to a section or the whole of the project, they may apply to the project manager or their representative under the contract for a completion certificate.

For many projects, sectional completion may signal the handover of a physical unit from one contractor to another for further work, fit-out or equipment installation. Well-defined procedures for such handovers should be established and agreed well in advance and should preferably form part of the relevant contractors' contracts.

Taking over (known as 'partial possession' in JCT contracts) is a much more informal arrangement and is used where the promoter did not envisage taking over part of the works at the start of the project.

Defects

Before acceptance of the works and issue of a completion certificate, the project manager or their representative under the contract should inspect the relevant works jointly with the contractor and prepare a list of outstanding items of work or defects. Together with a programme for completion of the work, the schedule should be agreed with both the contractor and the promoter or a follow-on contractor, as appropriate.

Documentation

The commissioning and handover state is the point for finalising the project documentation. There are six main categories of documents to be handed over by designers, equipment suppliers and contractors:

1 records of the equipment and services as installed
2 commissioning instructions, including safety rules
3 operating and maintenance (O&M) manuals
4 test certificates (e.g. the results of proof loading tests, pressure tests or ultrasonic tests of welds, etc.)
5 the health and safety file
6 legal agreements.

Generally, the first category will include design and performance specifications, test certificates, defects lists, as-built drawings and warranties. In addition to these, documents for commissioning and operation will include permits, certificates of insurances, warranties and handover certificates.

Acceptance, handover and certificates

Following achievement of the relevant performance test criteria, the project manager or their representative under the contract is normally required to issue a certificate of completion, or sectional completion as appropriate, to the promoter or other appropriate party to the contract depending on the exact legal status of 'ownership' of the resulting asset and the contractual details of the procurement strategy. This is accompanied by the relevant outstanding work schedule and completion programme. For complex projects, a handover certificate and detailed handover procedures may be used. Under many forms of contract, the issue of a completion certificate allows the release of part of the retention money held back by the promoter (or other appropriate party to the contract) from payments to the contractor.

Warranties and defects liability

In the UK, most of the contractor's responsibilities and general liabilities in respect of the works handed over pass to the promoter (or to another contractor following on to do other work) upon issue of the certificate of practical completion or handover. Thus, warranties for equipment, insurance liabilities and responsibility for operation, day-to-day cleaning, maintenance and health and safety may pass, as appropriate, to the project's promoter, or to a follow-on contractor, or to such mix of the promoter or asset owner and concessionaire and operating organisations as may be determined by the procurement regime and associated contractual agreement.

In many other countries, contractors and suppliers of equipment continue to have legal requirements to be insured against public liabilities.

Occupation

Planning

The occupation of a major asset, following the issue of its completion certificate, may in itself represent a significant project, requiring extensive planning and development, particularly for large purpose-built infrastructure assets. The occupation sequence may differ considerably from construction, in that it centres around employees themselves and involves both the style of management and the culture of the user's organisation.

Consultation with representatives of users and employees can therefore be important in project planning and design to identify their requirements and what facilities they require. Their involvement can also be important to ensure their commitment to the results and hence the ultimate success of the project.

Organisation and control

To ensure a successful occupation sequence, it is not uncommon for the promoter to appoint a dedicated occupation or 'migration' project team, headed by a project manager. Their responsibilities will include planning, programmes, budgets, methodologies, contingency plans, health, safety and control procedures and the identification of risks. Steering groups and representatives' groups may also be established to promote consultation and communication and assist with identification of requirements. The team will need to arrange support services and utilities and may also need to coordinate migration with continuing construction or fit-out work. They may also need to reconcile different interests of owners and occupiers.

REFERENCES AND FURTHER READING

Sharma R (2010) The Railway Network Young Professionals best paper seminar on sustainable, economical and safe solutions, *Testing and commissioning for a light rail project.*

Civil Engineering Procedure
ISBN 978-0-7277-6069-2

Chapter 10
Operation, maintenance and asset management

Operation and maintenance needs

Completion and handover of the project marks a significant point in the progression of the project life cycle; it is at this point that the project becomes a 'live asset' of the promoter. Some assets may subsequently require only regular inspection and maintenance, but more often they will become part of a portfolio of assets which, in order to deliver the promoter's original requirements, require regular planned preventative maintenance (PPM) and reactive maintenance (RM) interventions. Individual infrastructure facilities, for example a road, bridge or hospital, require not only inspection and maintenance, but also planning of their use in a wider highway or healthcare system. Temporary or partial closure for maintenance, refurbishment or replacement of components can affect traffic flows or healthcare provision across a wide area.

The delivery of an asset available for a promoter to use on a continuing basis requires careful consideration of both operational requirements and appropriate maintenance regimes at an early stage in the gestation of the project.

The annual cost of operating and maintaining infrastructure or facilities varies significantly and, depending on both design life and discount rate, may represent a similar order of magnitude as the initial capital cost on a net present value basis. Operations and maintenance regimes therefore need to be considered throughout the development of a project.

The costs to operate and maintain an asset clearly requires the economic consideration and understanding of the whole-life cost of that asset. Specifically, the design, construction, operation, maintenance, decommissioning and, in some cases, financing of the project need to be fully understood throughout various stages of a project's development. To ensure the asset remains in the appropriate condition upon completion and throughout its operational life, critical or sensitive elements of the asset will require periodic inspection to enable the assurance of the continued structural integrity, serviceability and fitness for purpose of the asset. The inspection regime will itself be in part dependent upon both the planned and actual operation of the asset and the extent to which the envisaged maintenance regime is realised.

The optimal whole-life cost will further depend on financial assumptions including, inter alia, cost forecasts over time and the discount rate chosen (sensitivity tests may be performed to help understand the impact of different discount rates) and may be further constrained by initial affordability considerations.

Planning for operation, maintenance and asset management
Economic considerations
The importance of considering the costs of operation and maintenance as an integral aspect of the design process was emphasised in Chapter 1. Differences in these costs between alternative schemes should influence the choice between them. Failure to consider these costs may lead to the selection of a design that is uneconomical to maintain, operators or decommission. Ensuring the health and safety of operators, consumers and third parties throughout the life cycle of the asset, including its operation, maintenance, refurbishment/reconfiguration and decommissioning, is clearly both a business necessity and regulatory requirement.

Operational and maintenance assumptions also affect the initial capital cost. In a water treatment asset, for example, the choice of ozone instead of chlorine as a disinfectant may increase the construction cost but reduce the operating cost.

Social and environmental sustainability
In addition to the consideration of whole-life costs, the environmental credentials of the project are important, particularly from a legislative, policy or funding perspective. Traditionally, promoters have sought to undertake an environmental impact assessment, as part of the planning process for schemes; however, a range of 'certification' procedures now exist to enable promoters and the design/construction team to demonstrate (and evidence) sustainable design and construction.

There are two mainstream sustainability assessment toolkits: CEEQUAL (for civil engineering) and BREAAM (for buildings). The international version is known by the acronym LEED. CEEQUAL aims to 'deliver improved project specification, design and construction of civil engineering works' and is designed to reward promoters, designers and contractors who strive to achieve high levels of environmental and social responsibility in their work. CEEQUAL uses a simple rating system to assess performance.

Flexibility
For projects with extended in-use life expectancy, it may be prudent to consider the effects of operational and maintenance change and to assess the extent to which the

project may be able to accommodate changes. Refurbishment and reconfiguration are often used to adjust or enhance capacity utilisation. While it is not possible to accurately predict the future, opportunities to allow flexibility in both asset operation and maintenance are often valued by promoters.

As-constructed drawings

As-constructed drawings should be prepared during construction, while detail can be seen and checked. For civil engineering work, this is often undertaken by the promoter's representative and their staff. For electrical, mechanical and process projects or elements it is frequently the contractor or a sub-contractor who prepares the drawings and submits them for approval by the promoter.

At practical completion, and not later, a fully detailed set of drawings (or a building information model) should be available to the promoter, to represent the works as-constructed. During the defects liability period, any remedial work should also be recorded. The drawings will be used to plan the use and control of the asset, maintenance and repair work, and as the basis of further design work for future development of the asset. The drawings handed over to the promoter at the completion of the contract must therefore be a reliable representation of the actual asset at that time.

Operation and maintenance (O&M) manuals

The drawings and other documents must specify the operation and maintenance of hardware (equipment and structures), software, and the supporting needs of planning, stock control, billing and revenue collection, customer and employee relationships, training and career development.

Building information modelling (BIM)

In projects where design and construction are coordinated using object-oriented modelling (also known as BIM), it is desirable that the federated model should be made available to the promoter for the purposes of effective asset management. Traditionally, the promoter is provided with the as-constructed drawings and the O&M manuals, but these documents lack the capability to assist the promoter in seeking optimal solutions for change of use, energy efficiency and facilities management (FM). The UK government has mandated the use of Level 2 BIM for all public civil engineering/building projects by 2016. This will require some consideration of how promoters will ensure that their requirements for an interoperable model are achieved throughout the project life cycle. BIM is covered in more detail in Chapter 11.

Asset management strategy

Asset management is concerned with the design and implementation of organisational systems that support the effective management of assets in alignment with corporate strategies and objectives. In large, complex organisations with responsibility for significant numbers of individual and groups of assets (Network Rail and Highways England are notable examples) asset management is a core business function. In 2014, ISO 55000 (ISO, 2014) was published to replace the better known PAS 55-1:2008 'Asset management' specification, which set out a 28-point requirements specification for establishing and verifying an optimised whole-life management system for 'all types of physical assets'.

Contracts for operation and maintenance

Increasingly, the promoters of projects are employing other organisations to manage the operation and maintenance of completed facilities. These FM contracts may be separate from those for design and construction, employing a following-on services contractor, or they may be part of a comprehensive contract for the project.

Process facilities, such as a water treatment plant comprising a reservoir, treatment asset and metered distribution network, require every component to have well defined contracts for their operation. The operational resources required, in the form of power, chemicals, labour and the collection of revenue, can result in complex operation and maintenance programmes.

Increasingly, promoters are integrating the obligations for operating and maintaining the asset with the contractor who supplied most or all of a project. The contractor should then have a greater incentive to provide an asset that will be of appropriate quality and operate effectively for the prescribed number of years, and ensure that skilled personnel will be available to train the promoter's operating staff before transfer. The scope of these contracts can include many different combinations of operation, maintenance, condition on handover and, in some instances, training and commission support.

Operation only

Under these contracts the operator undertakes to operate and manage the asset, with any maintenance being the responsibility of the promoter. A toll bridge, leisure complex or local road network could be examples, where the operator would be primarily concerned with ensuring the asset is available to function on a day-to-day basis but who may not be responsible for the associated maintenance regime. The cleaning of an office, the provision of a helpdesk, security or porterage services are examples of individual 'soft' FM services. These may be procured by the promoter on an individual service basis or bundled together to provide a single operational support interface.

Maintenance only

In this case the operator, usually the contractor, is responsible for solely the maintenance of the asset. Examples may be the maintenance of particular equipment which may be required due to wear and tear over a fixed period, for example the regular service of air handling fans or replacement of associated filters. Heating, ventilation, air conditioning, electrical and building fabric maintenance services are generally referred to as 'hard' facilities management. Similar to soft FM, hard FM services may be procured individually but are more often bundled together.

Case study 6: Optimising resurfacing – the 1000 T project – M5 junctions 6–9 northbound and southbound resurfacing

The austerity measures imposed by the UK coalition government to tackle the high levels of debt have had a significant impact on departmental budgets, including those of the former Highways Agency (now Highways England). Nevertheless, the government committed to a resurfacing programme as part of the strategic road network. The key challenge was to focus on keeping the road safe and serviceable while undertaking 'patching jobs' – this required a rethink around how the assets were maintained and the planning, scheduling and execution of the resurfacing work on site. This case study focuses on 'Area 9' in the Midlands, where Highways England worked in partnership with a number of supply-chain partners.

The object of this project was to optimise the surfacing outputs per shift and establish conditions for future schemes to increase resurfacing productivity. A specific target objective for the project was to lay 1000 tonnes of blacktop using one gang in one shift.

Data provided from laying records from the previous 6 months was analysed and established a baseline of 240 tonnes per shift per gang. This was supported by data collected from overnight visits to the site. The efficiency was determined by how long the paver was active during the time of the closure. From the site visits this was determined to be 33%. Graphical methods were used to monitor progress, which enabled the team to question areas that could be challenged and enable an increase in efficiency. The areas identified included the following:

1   Time between closing the motorway and starting the planning activity.
2   Time between the start of the planning activity and the paving activity.
3   The work completed considerably before the planned road reopening time.
4   The working window times.

To overcome these constraints, the team undertook the following:

1   Provision of traffic management to enable the equipment to be on site and ready by the time the road was closed.

2   Ensuring material was available for laying, enabling the paving to start 45 minutes after the planing started (was 1 hour 40 minutes).
3   Planning to extend the working time to fill the available working window.
4   Challenge the working windows and extend those where possible (mainly weekends).

As a consequence of the measures taken, the output per gang per shift was increased to an average 344 tonnes on the northbound stretch and then subsequently to an average 404 tonnes on the southbound stretch. The overall average during the scheme was 370 tonnes per shift per gang – an increase of 35% from the baseline of 240 tonnes.

A Saturday was selected offering a 13-hour working window (as opposed to the normal 8 hours). Implementing the identified learning points the team laid 1024 tonnes in one shift with one paver.

Learning points have further been collated and a plan has been established to transfer this learning to the rest of Highways England, continue to include the learning points into the current Area 9 programme, continue to challenge, look at the process from end to end (to include from quarry by way of design though to construction) and continue to challenge working patterns.

Operation and maintenance

Under these terms of contract, the operator undertakes to operate the asset and perform all routine and non-routine maintenance necessary to sustain the asset in full working order and to ensure the asset is handed over at the end of the contract in accordance with a pre-agreed condition state. In addition, the operator is responsible for the provision of spares and consumables. An example may be the operation and maintenance of a water treatment asset or the provision of all but clinical services in a hospital.

Operation, maintenance and training (OMT)

Here the operator is obliged to train personnel, usually the promoter's, to operate and maintain the asset until transfer. This form of contract may be considered for process or industrial plants that require high levels of operation and maintenance skills in order to ensure that both revenues and costs modelled in the promoter's feasibility assessment are capable of being achieved, is generated during and after the contract.

Government 'soft-landings' framework

While appropriate for buildings rather than civil infrastructure projects as such; the soft-landings framework illustrates the importance attached to ensuring assets are managed effectively during the early phases of use. The soft-landings framework involves the promoter appointing designers and constructors to contracts that go beyond practical completion – this is designed to assist facilities/building managers in overcoming the usual teething problems that occur when an asset becomes operational. The framework provides for a longer, less-intensive period of post-occupancy evaluation and intervention (typically 3 years). A range of established tools and techniques for post-occupancy evaluation (POE) can be used, including the design quality method (DQM).

Conditions of contract and risk

These long-term contracts thus differ significantly from construction contracts in their scope, duration, supervision, method of payment and the nature of risk taken by both the promoter and the contractor. The extent to which risk is born by the party best able to manage that risk will determine the delivery of optimal value for money.

NEC3 offers two contracts that are typically suitable for operation and maintenance contracts, the Term Service Contract (TSC) and the Term Service Short Contract (TSSC), the latter being appropriate for low-risk, low-complexity services.

In aggregate, the balancing of initial capital cost, annual operating costs, planned preventative and reactive maintenance costs, together with the expected life of the asset, discount rate and decommissioning costs leads to the optimal whole-life cost of the asset and the ideal allocation of risk.

Integrated contracts

The proliferation of build, own, operate and transfer (BOOT), design, build, finance and operate (DBFO) and the many associated variants has accelerated in the UK, primarily driven by the procurement of major government projects using public private partnerships (PPPs). In the majority of cases, the broad intent is for the promoter to procure the delivery of services for a period of time from a contractor rather than to procure or own a particular asset. The contractor in this case is often referred to as a special purpose company and typically includes a consortium of organisations which together have the ability to design, construct, operate, maintain and fund the project for a given concession period, for example 25 years. In theory, the asset is returned to the promoter in a pre-agreed condition state.

Training of operations personnel and managers

Training of operatives and managers may be part of an operation and maintenance contract. Training has two elements: the act of communicating knowledge and the act of receipt of knowledge. In many instances the latter is unfortunately disregarded as it can be difficult to quantify and assess in legal terms.

The first step in training must be to assess the existing skills of those who are to be trained. The training contract should clearly define how this should be achieved and against what criteria skills will be measured – in terms of quality as well as quantity. Trainees' effectiveness should be evaluated. The contract documentation must provide an appropriate mechanism for this.

The educational objectives of all training programmes should be specified in the contract. They should specify what the trainees will be expected to be competent to do, rather than what they should know. Job descriptions must be specific and unambiguous. Terms such as 'awareness' and 'understanding' should be avoided.

Training should not be considered to be an appendage to a contract designed to perform a dissimilar function. If training is to be included in the operation and maintenance contract, the human and material resources that will be allocated to training need to be defined. For the trainer, skills in interpersonal communication, sensitivity to different cultural norms and values, and knowledge of training methods are as important as technical competence.

Overseas operating contracts

Standards of operation and maintenance of many projects in both developed and developing countries vary considerably. Common problems include the use of inappropriate design and technology, inadequate organisations, and the low priority and status promoters may give to maintenance work.

Care must be taken to assess the factors that may affect maintenance on overseas projects. Difficulties may sometimes arise due to the cultural differences and/or scarcity of trained managers, technicians and craftsmen, a shortage of foreign exchange or interruption of supplies, power, spares or raw materials. The division of responsibility for these factors needs to be clearly defined in a contract.

FURTHER READING AND REFERENCES

Cook M (2007) *The Design Quality Manual*. Blackwell, Oxford, UK.

ISO (International Organization for Standardization) (2014) ISO 55000-1: 2014 Asset management. ISO, Geneva, Switzerland.

NEC3 (2013) Term Service Contract (TSC) Apr 2013 72 978 07277 5891 0.

Civil Engineering Procedure
ISBN 978-0-7277-6069-2

ICE Publishing: All rights reserved
http://dx.doi.org/10.1680/cep.60692.131

Chapter 11
Building information modelling (BIM)

Introduction

Building information modelling (BIM) emerged in the 1970s, principally from the work of Charles Eastman's 'Building Description System' (Eastman *et al.*, 2008). The popularisation of BIM in the early 2000s emerged principally in the USA and this allowed large firms in the States to gain an international 'first mover advantage', resulting in increased market shares (Saxon, 2013). However, the publication of the *Government Construction Strategy* by the Cabinet Office in 2011 has drastically increased BIM awareness and take-up in the UK. The strategy mandates the use of 'fully collaborative three-dimensional (3D) BIM' on all public sector construction projects by 2016 (BSI, 2013). This was set as a 5-year target in order to provide a phased process through which the government and the industry would work together to develop standards while allowing time for training (Cabinet Office, 2011).

Despite this, some confusion and contradictions exist, as do a large number of definitions. The UK government has purposefully avoided giving BIM a specific definition and instead uses a maturity diagram in order to convey what BIM means (BIM Task Group, 2013a). At the highest level of maturity, BIM is a process that involves producing and managing building information during the life cycle of an asset.

A semantic debate also exists, notably in the use of the term 'building' – this is a particular issue in civil engineering where the applications of BIM to infrastructure may not be fully recognised or appreciated (Race, 2013). There is also a widespread view that 'building information management' would be more appropriate given the emphasis on data exchange and collaboration.

Maturity levels

Figure 11.1 illustrates the different maturity phases, with a focus on the level of collaboration achieved at each stage and across the project life cycle. The UK government requirement is that all parts of the project must operate at Level 2 or above (NBS, 2013).

Level 0 – 2D CAD drawings are used without a standardised approach.
Level 1 – as seen in Figure 11.1, both 2D and 3D models can be used, but collaboration is limited.

Figure 11.1 BIM maturity levels based on the original Bew/Richard wedge and Dassault Systèmes 3DEXPERIENCE platform

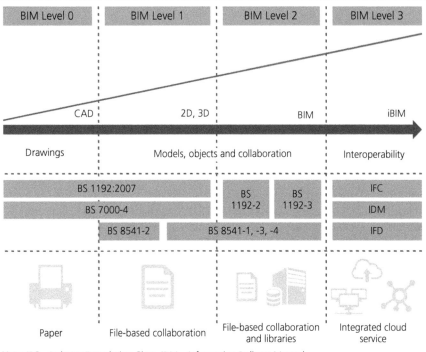

Note: IFC – Industry Foundation Class, IDM – Information Delivery Manual,
IFD – International Framework for Dictionaries

- Level 2 – this level will by mandatory by 2016. Different teams use separate building information models but standards are used to ensure that the models are constructed logically. This enables other designers to use the same model (Sinclair, 2012). The BSI (2013) states that the definition of Level 2 will evolve, but still centre around the separate building information models operating in a common data environment.
- Level 3 – this is often termed 'the holy grail of BIM' or integrated BIM (iBIM). All parties (architects, structural engineers, contractors and so on) use the same building information model. This requires software interoperability and the development of current contracts used by the industry.

Dimensions

In moving up the 'maturity curve', it is envisioned that dimensions beyond 2D and 3D will be added to building information models:

- 4D – time is added to the 3D model. This enables visualisation of the entire construction process and not just the finished product. This has the potential to improve scheduling and project management.
- 5D – cost is added to the 4D model. This could provide real time cost estimates that would change when the model changes.
- 6D – the higher dimensions (6, 7 and potentially even more) appear not to be well defined yet. BIMTalk (2012) refers to 6D as 'sustainability' and 7D as 'facility management', while 6D is often defined as facilities management (Redbike Systems, 2013).

Regardless, facilities management is an area where information regarding the operation and maintenance of the structure is incorporated into the model. This has been identified as an area in the *GovernmentConstruction Strategy* (Cabinet Office, 2011) that has the potential to drastically reduce life cycle costs. A dimension that includes sustainability would include information regarding carbon footprint.

Defining BIM

Many attempts were made to define BIM in the 1990s, but one commonality was their technology centricity (Race, 2013). The millennium saw a new understanding of BIM emerge as the benefits of enhanced data sharing, collaboration and cloud computing could revolutionise the whole sector and the way the different actors (architects, engineers, etc.) interact. Traditionally, these actors work in silos, often with contrasting agendas. BIM can potentially create a more collaborative atmosphere through integrating different siloes and thus unifying the industry (Zhenzhong *et al.*, 2008). As this was realised, new definitions started to arise that shifted the focus away from technology towards 'polices', 'processes', 'management' and 'methodology'.

The ICE published a policy statement in 2012 that describes BIM as 'the purposeful management of information through the whole life cycle of an infrastructure asset'. The statement further emphasises the collaborative working aspects of BIM, describing it as 'a managed approach to the collection and exploitation of information across the life cycle of a built environment asset'. A key aspect of BIM are the object oriented computer-generated models containing data related to the design, construction and operation of the asset.

Advantages of BIM

Level 2 BIM is forecasted to save the government 20% on construction capital expenditure (capex) (BIM Task Group, 2013a) and impact 15% of the UK GDP (Saxon, 2013). The savings in capex is normally quoted as the main reason for implementation, but Cabinet Office (2011) recognises that even larger savings can potentially be made in the operational stage of projects. The National Institute of Standards and Technology

(NIST) report (2004) shows that when measured over the entire life cycle, this is where the majority of costs are incurred.

There are many other potential benefits arising from BIM, besides cost reductions. There are certainly overlaps with cost reductions, but the US General Services Administration recognises quality, accuracy, coordination and efficiency as the main benefits of BIM (GSA, 2007).

Another advantage of BIM implementation in the UK is international competition. The USA is widely viewed as the international leader in the field of BIM, thus creating a distinct competitive advantage. The 2011 *Government Construction Strategy* has changed this balance and it is believed that BIM expertise is set to become an exportable skill for the UK (Kemp, 2014). It is hoped that the UK will have a strong position to export this expertise to the rest of Europe (Race, 2013). Ideally, BIM adoption would lead to UK firms gaining a larger market share of the global construction segment as well, which is forecasted to grow by 70% by 2025 (HM Government, 2015). This growth is projected to occur in the developing world, particularly in China, which is very enthusiastic about BIM (Race, 2013).

Various researchers have shown additional benefits. By collecting questionnaires, Yan and Damain (2008) have shown how industry professionals consider improved sustainability, creativity, human resource efficiency and time efficiency to result from BIM. The same survey also showed that the participants considered 'waste of time and human resource' to be one of the main drawbacks of BIM, again highlighting confusion and conflicting ideas of what BIM actually is.

Current building information models are object-based and are the result of over 40 years of development and research in the area of computational 3D design. It started in the late 1960s with software that allowed the creation of simple polyhedral shapes, while today, these models can edit themselves according to the definitions used to describe them (Eastman *et al.*, 2011).

In the digital world, an object is defined as 'an instance of class' (Race, 2013). In a construction context, this simply translates into objects being digital versions of construction components, with set attributes. In BIM, all these objects will be defined through dimensions, material and descriptions. The description could, for example, include information about the object's weight, facilitating the planning for contractors, or chemical content, which might be relevant for health and safety precautions. Pertinent information with regards to health and safety could be integrated into objects from the very start of the project (Mordue and Finch, 2014). BIM objects will also include characteristics.

BIM libraries offer a way to avoid in-house creation of BIM objects; the library growing at the fastest rate in the UK is the free NBS national library and it has an array of objects ranging from building systems to mechanical to electrical objects. This can save time but does not necessarily compromise flexibility as specific project data can still be added to the objects (Mordue and Finch, 2014).

Interoperability

Construction output is the result of team effort, where many activities are underpinned by proprietary software. In order for BIM to be efficiently collaborative, it is necessary for multiple pieces of software to be able to use the same data. This is called interoperability and is a key ingredient of BIM. Interoperability will eliminate manual copying of data between different computational applications. This is desirable as manual copying will introduce errors and deters iteration; a crucial tool for developing optimum solutions. The industry has been using translators for geometric information, such as DXF, IGES or SAT. However, these translators are not sufficient as BIM uses a lot more data than CAD; geometry, attributes and properties are included in the model. One way to allow for interoperability in BIM is by using a neutral exchange format, like Industry Foundation Classes (IFC) (Eastman *et al.*, 2011).

IFC and buildingSMART

The history of IFC dates back to 1994, when the Industry Alliance for Interoperability was created (Bazjanac and Crawley, 1998). The formation of this consortium was initiated by AutoCAD and it was made up of 12 major US companies (buildingSMART, 2014b). It opened up membership for other organisations the following year and became a global organisation in 1996. The name was changed in 1997 to International Alliance for Interoperability (IAI). The new international organisation was registered as non-profit and its aim is to develop and publish IFC (Eastman *et al.*, 2011). During a meeting in Norway, IAI was renamed to buildingSMART after it was realised in 2005 that the previous name was too convoluted. As of 2009 buildingSMART was a truly international organisation; it has 450 corporate members from 18 different countries (Eastman *et al.*, 2011).

IFC allows for interoperability between software applications by providing a means of transferring building information from one actor to another without any loss of data integrity. Another major advantage of IFC is that it is 'open-source' in nature (Mordue and Finch, 2014). The IFC schema is still under development and as such has some shortcomings. Eastman *et al.* (2011) identify some of them in the version released in 2010 as follows:

- In relation to geometries, rules and constraints cannot be exchanged.
- There is a lack of properties.
- Some properties need special editing.

■ Object classes are not defined to the same level of detail for fabrication and manufacturing as they are for architectural purposes.

IDM

In order to realise the full benefits of BIM, inter-team communication needs to be improved. The information communicated needs to be of the right quality and supplied at the right time. This can only be achieved if there is a consensus on the building process and the information requirements.

The type of information needed has been addressed by IFC as it offers a reference to the information involved. However, it does not integrate this with the building process; this is where the information delivery manual (IDM) comes in. IDM seeks to integrate information with processes; this is done in three steps:

1 Pinpoint the processes that make up construction.
2 Find out what information is needed to enable these processes.
3 Assess the result of the process being carried out.

This will act as a catalyst for BIM implementation as it will give stakeholders access to easily understandable information about the processes involved, the information involved and the outcomes.

Information management

When a project utilises the benefits of BIM, it procures information about the built asset as well as the built asset itself. The project brief deals with the built asset while the employer's information request (EIR) deals with the information about the asset. How to manage this information is covered in PAS 1192-2 (BSI, 2013), which outlines what information is needed at different stages of a project in regards to BIM.

The requirements of the employer in terms of BIM are covered in the EIR. The BIM execution plan (BEP) is then used to show that the suppliers can meet these requirements. It is decided what information has to be delivered at what stages in 'data drops'. Information is then sent to the promoter at certain stages during the delivery phases of the project and it is up to the promoter to decide what to do; if progress has been satisfactory, or if the project needs to be put on hold and so on. At handover, all information will be handed over to the promoter, where all non-graphical information is in the form of a COBie file (BSI, 2013). This information can then be used for facilities management and added to if the building asset is altered.

It is difficult to assess how effective this process is, as it is relatively new and the literature on the subject is limited. Krieger (2013) highlights some issues about inconsistencies in the BEP but also outlines steps for how to use it more effectively, including educating the client and creating a schedule of expectations.

Employer's information request

The EIR enables the details of the building information models and the information management process to be included in the tender process. It sets out the models that need to be produced, the aim of these models and what level of detail is needed at the different stages (BIM Task Group, 2013b).

BIM execution plan

The BEP is a document provided by the supplier to show how the EIR will be met. There are two versions of the BEP; one submitted for tendering and one once the contract has been awarded (National Federation of Builders, 2013). The one submitted before contract award is made up of the supplier's proposed approach while the post-contract award BEP demonstrates commitment from all involved parties. The details of the post-contract BEP will evolve during the project as the supply chain gets confirmed (Gleeds, 2014).

The BEP allocates responsibilities during each stage of a project with regards to BIM (Building and Construction Authority, 2013). It provides a detailed outline of how the project will be carried out, inspected and coordinated. This is done to ensure that all parts of the project team are aware of their responsibilities (BIM Acceleration Committee, 2014) and so that the promoter is satisfied that the suppliers have the right capability to meet the EIR. If the EIR is not met, negotiations need to take place, where the promoter might have to compromise on demands (BSI, 2013). The pre-contract BEP will include everything defined in the EIR in addition to the project implementation plan, targets for levels of cooperation, targets for information models, milestones and the project information model strategy (BIM Acceleration Committee, 2014). The post-contract BEP will include more details along with the master information delivery plan (BSI, 2013).

Level of detail

The level of detail (LOD) required at certain data drops is outlined in the model production and delivery table, together with the assignment of duty for arranging the models. LOD determines the permitted purpose and the content of a model, making it important to specify it correctly. It is then the obligation of the project team to create the models defined to the established LOD in the Model Production and Delivery Table (MPDT) (BIM Task Group, 2013d).

COBie

COBie stands for Construction Operations Building Information Exchange and orignates from the USA. Its development started under the auspices of NASA and the

White House Office of Science and has later been supported by the General Services Administration and the Corps of Engineers (Race, 2013).

COBie has been chosen as the exchange format used for non-graphical information in the UK due to its potential compatibility with IFC, ease of access for users and cost (Hamil, 2011). The information within COBie can be easily accessed as Excel spreadsheets (East, 2014). This will create a very high number of rows even on smaller projects, and on larger ones are known to have reached Excel's ultimate capacity (Race, 2013). However, COBie is not meant to be noticed, rather COBie will act as a system-to-system information exchange; this process does not involve manual input (BSI, 2013). Once implemented, COBie will just receive the attention of software developers; it will be an enabling background technology (National Institute of Building Sciences, 2015).

The information in COBie will be transferred to the client at the information handover, at the end of the delivery stages (Eastman *et al.*, 2011). Without COBie, the information handed over to the promoter is generally in the form of large amounts of paper (East, 2007) and it is prepared in an expedient manner and is not organised systematically. COBie provides a standardised approach to collecting and delivering consistent information. Data are first gathered from designers in the initial stages, and then by contractors as the construction is carried out. This information is well structured and categorised logically (Malleson *et al.*, 2012).

Case study 7: A160/A180 Port of Immingham improvements

Highways England (formerly the Highways Agency) is a 'government company' responsible for modernising and maintaining the highways, running the network and keeping traffic moving on motorways and major 'A-roads' (known as trunk routes). It has devised a BIM strategy within its project and asset management activities, including earmarking a number of projects as 'early adopters' to develop the required systems, software, protocols and capabilities, which are not currently widely used in the highways sector. The A160/A180 Port of Immingham Improvement project (Figure 11.2) has been selected as one such early adopter.

In line with government expectations, the project is developing BIM to a minimum of Level 2 compliance, with some elements of Level 3 being explored. To achieve this, the following deliverables are being progressed:

- 2D information – 2D drawings where required are output directly from the 3D model while specification appendices are prepared in the usual fashion.
- 3D design model – a fully federated 3D model of the scheme has been produced and is to be maintained throughout the duration of the scheme.

This model will be used for coordination, communication and clash management.

- 4D programme model – the programme is now being embedded into elements of the model for construction purposes. The initial target for full integration will be the rail bridge and Town Street bridge. For the rail bridge, focused construction methodologies are visualised and digital prototyping used to demonstrate the breakdown of the construction into small timescale intervals. This is providing confidence to Network Rail and will time check deliverables for operational monitoring during the possession.

- 5D cost model – budget and forecast are to be integrated into the model on a trial basis, starting with Town Street bridge and the rail bridge. This will be used for earned value management, valuing change and optimising visibility of cost. This breaks down into two elements:
  - First, taking off the quantities – for this they are developing the capabilities within the primary modelling software (Civil 3D and Revit) as well as trialling third party software such as CANDY and VICO.
  - Second, the costs are attached so that a forecast can be produced. Output of this will be compared to a forecast achieved from conventional means. This will be used to run P6 EVA Trial.

- 6D asset model – as an early adopter the project is working closely with the Asset Management Office (AMO) to correctly define asset requirements, now and in future systems. This is undertaken by the BIM coordinator and involves fully understanding the existing Highways England databases and the proposals of AMO for the IAM IS proposed database. This will ensure that for the trial section, there will be a fully functioning set of BIM data. It is noted that if this element is not correctly delivered we only achieve project information modelling (PIM) and not BIM. For this work they are investigating the principles of COBie standards as the transfer mechanism to tie the asset data to the model.

Asset tagging

Working with Red-Bite to trial a state-of-the-art asset tagging system generated through part of a UK government initiative. Deployment is a plug and play process requiring nothing more than readers with network connectivity. Radio frequency identification (RFID) and sensor devices connect directly to the cloud with no onsite middleware or hardware and so the costs of RFID network management are reduced by as much as 85%. Through this initiative, every reader and 'Internet of Things' device in the network can be viewed and controlled remotely. Tag reads, faults, uptime and current status can all be viewed online and in real time. All configurations, software and feature updates are carried out remotely.

Mobile technology
The project is making use of the latest mobile technology, allowing access in any location to the 3D model for interrogation, marking out, measurements and direct querying with the wider team. Information is able to be obtained direct from the model and all paper forms are currently being made electronic, including signature inputs.

Data storage and business collaboration
ProjectWise has been utilised on the project for all data storage. This provides the capacity to accommodate the model files so that we have the opportunity to link data to the model.

Sustainability inputs
The project will finalise opportunities to look at solid modelling techniques (e.g. Solidworks) to assess the level of embodied carbon within the scheme design and construction. An example of this is information received from pavement contractors of the carbon attached to their supply of material. This will enable the scheme to demonstrate how we can quantify and identify the carbon footprint of the scheme and the impact of any proposed changes.

Other BIM initiatives
- Using BIM for target cost.
- Identifying and providing EIRs.
- Using BIM for road safety audits.
- Exporting data from the 3D model for site setting out purposes.
- Engagement with managing agent contractor to align data attributes for safety inspection handover.

The following strategic objectives are monitored against to ensure that the deployment of BIM is continuously adding value:

- Safety increased through the early identification and clear markings of site hazards prior to construction along with finding clashes onsite, preventing potentially dangerous situations.
- Collaboration with the whole project team working together to meet the client's objectives for the project and final asset.
- Integration of systems and approach to maximise the seamless reuse of information throughout the project life cycle.

- Efficiency by having correct, complete information available in a timely fashion.
- Coordination to reduce spatial conflicts ('clashes') and missing information in the construction information, and thereby reducing delays.
- Optimisation through maximising prefabrication and modularisation opportunities.
- Waste reduction with a 'design and build once' ethos, reducing abortive work and resource wastage through fewer mistakes and use of off-site manufacture.
- Accuracy to avoid delays in construction due to clashes, conflicts or missing or inaccurate information.
- Knowledge by using their 'early adopter' status to develop best practice and share learning throughout Highways England and the wider industry.

Figure 11.2 Scope of A160/A180 Port of Immingham improvements

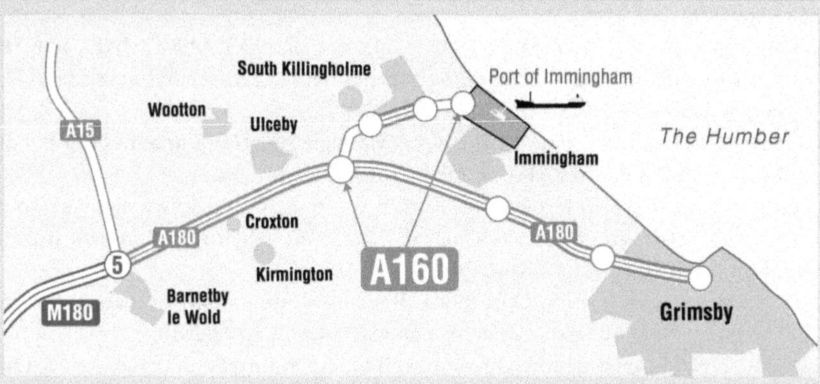

FURTHER READING AND REFERENCES

Bazjanac V and Crawley DB (1998) *The Implementation of Industry Foundation Classes in Simulation Tools for the Building Industry.* http://www.ibpsa.org/proceedings/bs1997/bs97_p125.pdf (accessed 18 December 2014).

BIM Acceleration Committee (2014) Appendix F I – Project BIM Execution Plan – example. http://www.buildingvalue.co.nz/sites/default/files/New-Zealand-BIM-Handbook-Appendix-F-i-Project-BIM-Execution-Plan-example.pdf (accessed 18 April 2015).

BIMTalk (2012) Bim_glossary:multidimbimjpg. http://bimtalk.co.uk/_detail/bim_glossary:multidimbim.jpg?id = bim_glossary%3Abim_dimensions (accessed 13 April 2015).

BIM Task Group (2013a) Frequently Asked Questions [online]. Available at: http://www.bimtaskgroup.org/bim-faqs/ (accessed 7 April 2015).

BIM Task Group (2013b) Welcome to the BIM Task Group Website [Online]. Available at: http://www.bimtaskgroup.org/ (accessed 18 April 2014).

BIM Task Group (2013c) BIM Employer's Information Requirements (EIR) [Online]. Available at: http://www.bimtaskgroup.org/bim-eirs/ (accessed 18 April 2015).

BIM Task Group (2013d) Building Information Model (BIM) Protocol [Online]. Available at: http://www.bimtaskgroup.org/wp-content/uploads/2013/02/The-BIM-Protocol.pdf (accessed 18 April 2015).

BSI (British Standards Institution) (2013) PAS 1192-2:2013 Incorporating Corrigendum No. 1. Specification for information management for the capital/delivery phase of construction projects using building information modelling. British Standards Institution, London, UK.

Building and Construction Authority (2013) *BIM Essential Guide for BIM Execution Plan.* http://www.corenet.gov.sg/media/586149/Essential-Guide-BEP.pdf (accessed 5 October 2015).

buildingSmart (2014a) General questions about buildingSMART, IAI, and IFC. http://www.buildingsmart-tech.org/implementation/faq/faq-general-questions#Q3 (accessed 17 December 2014).

buildingSMART (2014b) History. http://www.buildingsmart.org/about/about-building smart/history-2/ (accessed 18 December 2014).

Cabinet Office (2011) *Government Construction Strategy.* https://www.gov.uk/government/uploads/system/uploads/attachment_data/file/61152/Government-Construction-Strategy_0.pdf (accessed 13 April 2015).

East B (2014) Construction-Operations Building Information Exchange (COBie). http://www.wbdg.org/resources/cobie.php (accessed 18 April 2015).

East EW (2007) Construction Operations Building Information Exchange (COBie) Requirements Definition and Pilot Implementation Standard. Engineer Research and Development Center, Washington DC, USA.

Eastman C, Teicholz P, Sacks R and Liston K (2011) *BIM Handbook: A Guide to Building Information Modeling for Owners, Managers, Designers, Engineers, and Contractors* (2nd edn). Wiley, Hoboken, NJ, USA.

Gleeds (2014) *Thinking About BIM Paper 6.* http://www.gleeds.com/assets/Global/DownloadThinking_about_BIMpaper_6.pdf (accessed 18 April 2015).

GSA (General Services Administration) (2007) GSA BIM Guide Overview. http://www.gsa.gov/graphics/pbs/GSA_BIM_Guide_v0_60_Series01_Overview_05_14_07.pdf (accessed 14 April 2015).

Hamil S (2011) What is COBie? http://www.thenbs.com/topics/BIM/articles/whatIs COBie.asp (accessed 18 April 2015).

HM Government (2015) *Digital Built Britain Level 3 Building Information Modelling - Strategic Plan.* https://www.gov.uk/government/uploads/system/uploads/attachment_

data/file/410096/bis-15-155-digital-built-britain-level-3-strategy.pdf (accessed 14 April 2015).

Kemp D (2014) BIM an 'exportable skill' for UK contractors in emerging economies. *Construction News*, 17 October. https://global.factiva.com (accessed 18 April 2015).

Krieger J (2013) 'My BIM Journey' – 6 Lessons From a BIM/VDC Expert. *Building Design & Construction*. http://www.bdcnetwork.com/my-bim-journey-%E2%80%93-6-lessons-bimvdc-expert (accessed 26 April 2015).

Malleson A, Mordue S and Hamil S (2012) *The IFC/COBie Report 2012*. http://www.thenbs.com/pdfs/IFC_COBie-Report-2012.pdf (accessed 18 April 2015).

Mordue S and Finch R (2014) *BIM for Construction Health and Safety*. RIBA Publishing, Newcastle, UK.

NIST (National Institute of Standards and Technology) (2004) *Cost Analysis of Inadequate Interoperability in the US Capital Facilities Industry*. NIST, Boulder, CO, USA.

National Federation of Builders (2013) An Introduction to BIM Execution Planning (BEP). http://builders.org.uk/resources/nfb/000/322/399/BIM_Execution_Planning_Webinar_Oct_13.pdf (accessed 18 April 2015).

NBS (2013) *BIM Explained*. NBS, Newcastle-upon-Tyne, UK.

Race S (2013) *BIM Demystified: An Architect's Guide to Building Information Modelling/Management (BIM)*, 2nd edn. RIBA Publishing, London, UK.

Redbike Systems (2013) Dimensions of BIM. http://www.redbike.com.au/knowledge/dimensionsofbim.aspx (accessed 13 April 2015).

Saxon RG (2013) *Growth through BIM*. Construction Industry Council, London, UK.

Sinclair D (2012) *BIM Overlay to the RIBA Outline Plan of Work*. RIBA Publishing, London, UK.

Yan H and Damian P (2008) Benefits and Barriers of Building Information Modelling. http://www.hetnationaalbimplatform.nl/files/pages/294_benefits-and-barriers-of-building-information-modelling.pdf (accessed 18 December 2014).

Zhenzhong H, Jianping Z and Ziyin D (2008) Construction Process Simulation and Safety Analysis Based on Building Information Model and 4D Technology. *Tsinghua Science and Technology* **13(S1)**: 277–272, IEEE Xplore. http://ieeexplore.ieee.org (accessed 18 December 2014).

Civil Engineering Procedure
ISBN 978-0-7277-6069-2

Appendix A
Conditions of contract for civil engineering

Conditions of contract exist to provide the terms of engagement and to establish the responsibilities of the parties to the execution of a civil engineering project. The various contracts establish, inter alia, a formal system of communications between the parties, the allocation of risks and the detail of procedures and liabilities. Many of these contracts are often called 'standards' in the UK. It is arguable that 'models' is a more accurate description given the predisposition of promoters to modify contracts to meet their specific needs or those of the projects. Table A.1 lists the principal models, that illustrate contract arrangements in practice. Readers are advised to consult the websites of the publishing bodies where more detailed information can be obtained, including guidance notes on contract selection and procurement strategy.

The Royal Institution of Chartered Surveyors (RICS) draft guidance note – *Appropriate Contract Selection* (1st edn) – is available through the RICS and is recommended for further reading.

Table A.1 Conditions for contract for use in civil engineering works

ICC	The Infrastructure Conditions of Contract 2011, published by the Association for Consultancy and Engineering (ACE) and the Civil Engineering Contractors' Association (CECA) is a suite of contracts, with the 'measurement' version based on the former ICE (7th edn) Conditions of Contract. Other variants include: ■ Design and Construct contract ■ Term contract ■ Minor Works contract ■ Target Cost contract ■ Ground Investigation contract ■ Archaeological Investigation version ■ Partnering agreement.
NEC3	The New Engineering Contract (3rd ed.), published by Thomas Telford Limited. NEC3 is a 'family' of contracts. The Engineering and Construction Contract (ECC) is the principal contract and is comprised of a series of 'main option clauses':

- Option A – priced contract with activity schedule
- Option B – priced contract with bill of quantities
- Option C – target contract with activity schedule
- Option D – target contract with bill of quantities
- Option E – cost reimbursable contract
- Option F – management contract.

In addition to the 'main options', a series of 'secondary option clauses' are available to accommodate particular risks and uncertainties associated with a project:

- X1 – price adjustment for inflation
- X2 – changes in law
- X3 – multiple currencies (used only with options A and B)
- X4 – parent company guarantee
- X5 – sectional completion
- X6 – bonus for early completion
- X7 – delay damages
- X12 – partnering
- X13 – performance bond
- X14 – advanced payment to the contractor
- X15 – limitation of the contractor's design liability to reasonable skill and care
- X16 – retention (not used with option F)
- X17 – low performance damages
- X18 – limitation of liability
- X20 – key performance indicators (not used with option X12).

In addition to the ECC, NEC3 includes a suite of alternative arrangements to suit particular contractual situations:

- Adjudicator's Contract (AC)
- Engineering and Construction Short Contract (ECSC)
- Engineering and Construction Sub-contract
- Framework Agreement (FA)
- Term Service Contract (TSC)
- Terms Service Short Contract (TSSC).

CECA   The Civil Engineering Contractors' Association (CECA) provides a set of sub-contracts to support the latest version of the Infrastructure Conditions of Contract:

- form of sub-contract for use in conjunction with the Infrastructure Conditions of Contract (Design and Construct), 2011
- form of sub-contract for use in conjunction with the Infrastructure Conditions of Contract (Measurement), 2011.

GC/Works/1   GC/Works 1 Building & Civil Engineering Major Works, published by HM Stationery Office:

- Lump Sum with Quantities version 1998
- Lump Sum without Quantities version 1998

■ Single Stage Design and Build version 1998

■ Two Stage Design and Build 1998.

Note: GC/Works have not been updated since 1998 to reflect the government preference for NEC3. This form would require substantial updating before use to comply with contemporary legislation in the UK.

JCT 2011   Joint Contracts Tribunal (JCT) Standard Form of Building Contract, published by JCT Ltd (2011 edition). The contract family covers a range of procurement arrangements:

■ Standard Building Contract Without Quantities (SBC/XQ)

■ Standard Building Contract With Approximate Quantities (SBC/AQ)

■ Standard Building Sub-Contract Agreement (SBCSub/A)

■ Standard Building Sub-Contract Conditions (SBCSub/C)

■ Standard Building Sub-Contract with Sub-Contractor's Design Agreement (SBCSub/D/A)

■ Standard Building Sub-Contract with Sub-Contractor's Design Conditions (SBCSub/D/C)

■ Sub-Subcontract (SubSub)

■ Short Form of Sub-contract (ShortSub)

For major projects, which will combine civil engineering with building works, JCT provides separate contracts:

■ Major Project Construction Contract (MP)

■ Major Project Sub-contract (MPSub).

In addition to these main contracts, JCT provides separate forms for management (Management Contracting and Construction Management), Intermediate Contract, Design and Build Contract, Prime Cost and Measured Term Contracts. JCT additionally publish in cooperation with Constructing Excellence.

IChemE   The Institution of Chemical Engineers (IChemE) publishes contracts for use in the UK and internationally and are used for a wide range of process industries and in the construction of performance-based plant:

■ IChemE Form of Contract for Lump Sum Contracts (the 'Red Book') (5th edn), 2013

■ IChemE Form of Contract for Reimbursable Contracts (the 'Green Book') (4th edn), 2013

■ IChemE Form of Contract for Target Cost Contracts (the 'Burgundy Book') (2nd edn), 2013

■ IChemE Form of Contract for Minor Works (the 'Orange Book') (2nd edn), 2003 (reprinted 2006)

■ IChemE Form of Contract for Subcontracts (the 'Yellow Book') (4th edn), 2013

■ IChemE Form of Contract for Civil Engineering Subcontracts (the 'Brown Book') (3rd edn), 2013.

IET, IMechE (and formerly IEE)	MF/1, MF/2, MF/3 and MF/4 are a suite of contracts for electrical supply works, published by the Institution of Mechanical Engineers and the Institution of Engineering and Technology. Some of these contracts were first published in cooperation with the former Institution of Electrical Engineers.

- ▨ MF/1 Model Form of Contract for the design, supply and installation of electrical, electronic and mechanical plant, MF/1 (Rev 6) 2014
- ▨ MF/2 Model Form of General Conditions of Contract for use in connection with home or overseas contracts for the supply of electrical, electronic or mechanical plant (Rev. 1) 1999
- ▨ MF/3 Model Form of General Conditions of Contract to cover the main conditions for home contracts for the supply of electrical and mechanical goods – without erection (lump-sum) 2001
- ▨ MF/4 is a key industry Model Form of Terms and Conditions of Engagement for use as home or overseas agreements for the provision of consultancy services by engineering consultants.

Professional services contracts

ACE	Conditions of Engagement – to form the basis for an agreement between client and consulting engineer for one or more stages of a project. Association of Consulting Engineers, revised 2009
APM	Standard Terms for the Appointment of a Project Manager – with a schedule of duties and responsibilities for the construction industry. Association for Project Management 1998
NEC3	Professional Services Contract, 2005
NEC3	Adjudicator's Contract, 2005

International construction

FIDIC	The International Federation of Consulting Engineers (commonly known as FIDIC, acronym for its French name Fédération Internationale des Ingénieurs-Conseils) provides a range of international standard contracts, some of which bear similarities to UK-based models.

- ▨ The Red Book: Conditions of Contract for Construction for Building and Engineering Works Designed by the Employer
- ▨ The Yellow Book: Conditions of Contract for Plant and Design-Build
- ▨ The Silver Book: Conditions of Contract for EPC/Turnkey Projects
- ▨ The Green Book: Short Form of Contract
- ▨ The Blue Book: Contract for Dredging and Reclamation Works
- ▨ The Pink Book: Conditions of Contract for Construction for Building and Engineering Works Designed by the Employer (for bank-financed projects only)
- ▨ The White Book: Client/Consultant Model Services Agreement
- ▨ The Gold Book: FIDIC Design, Build and Operate Projects.

Definitions used in model conditions of contract

Table A.2 lists some of the equivalent definitions used in the more common model sets of conditions of contract for larger projects. These are approximate equivalents, dependent on their definition in the particular conditions of contract.

Table A.2 Definitions used in model conditions of contract

ICC and FIDIC (civil engineering)	NEC3	GC/Works/1	JCT2011	IChemE	MF/1, MF/2, MF/3 and MF/4
Employer	Employer	Employer	Employer	Purchaser	Purchaser
Contractor	Contractor	Contractor	Contractor	Contractor	Contractor
Engineer	Project manager Adjudicator Supervisor	Project manager Adjudicator	Architect or contract administrator	Project manager	Engineer
Engineer's representative (ICC) Engineer's assistants (FIDIC)		Clerk of works or resident engineer	Clerk of works	Project manager's representative	Engineer's representative
Contractor's agent (ICC) Contractor's representative (FIDIC)		Contractor's agent	Person-in-charge	Site manager	Contractor's representative
Tender total (ICC) contract price (FIDIC)	Prices	Contract sum	Contract sum	Contract price	Contract price
Contractor's equipment (ICC)	Equipment	Contractor's plant	Contractor's plant	Contractor's equipment	Contractor's equipment
Interim certificate (ICC) Interim payment certificate (FIDIC)	Payment certificate	Advances on account	Interim certificate	Interim Statement	Interim certificate
Final certificate	Payment certificate after completion of the whole works	Final certificate for payment	Final certificate	Final certificate	Final certificate of payment
Certificate of substantial completion (ICC) Taking over certificate (FIDIC)	Completion	Certificate of completion of the works	Practical completion certificate	Take-over certificate	Taking-over certificate

Table A.2 Continued

ICC and FIDIC (civil engineering)	NEC3	GC/Works/1	JCT2011	IChemE	MF/1, MF/2, MF/3 and MF/4
Defects correction period (ICC) Defects notification period (FIDIC)	Defect correction period	Maintenance period	Rectification period	Defects liability period	Defects liability period
Defects correction certificate (ICC) Performance certificate (FIDIC)	Defects certificate		Certificate of completion of making good	Final certificate	Final certificate of payment

Civil Engineering Procedure
ISBN 978-0-7277-6069-2

ICE Publishing: All rights reserved
http://dx.doi.org/10.1680/cep.60692.151

Appendix B
Further reading

The following references are suggested further reading on key topics covered throughout this book. The list is by no means exhaustive; the ICE Virtual Library provides a useful portal to digital content across the range of disciplines and is accessible at http://www. icevirtuallibrary.com.

The promotion of projects

Allport RJ (2010) *Planning Major Projects*. ICE Publishing, London, UK.

Griffith A, King A and Knight A (2003) *Best Practice Tendering for Design and Build Projects*. Thomas Telford, London, UK.

Hamilton A (2001) *Managing Projects for Success: A Trilogy*. Thomas Telford, London, UK.

Hoffman SL (2007) *The Law and Business of International Project Finance: A Resource for Governments, Sponsors, Lawyers and Project Participants* (3rd ed). Cambridge University Press, Cambridge, UK.

Kamara JM, Anumba CJ and Evbuomwan NF (2002) *Capturing Client Requirements in Construction Projects*. ICE Publishing, London, UK.

Scanlon B (1994) *Marketing of Engineering Services*. Thomas Telford, London, UK.

Risk management

Boussabaine AH and Kirkham RJ (2004) *Whole Life-cycle Costing: Risk and Risk Responses*. Blackwell, Oxford, UK.

HM Treasury (2004) *The Orange Book Management of Risk – Principles and Concepts*. HMSO, London, UK.

Institution of Civil Engineers and Institute and Faculty of Actuaries (2014) *Risk Analysis and Management for Projects (RAMP)* (3rd edn). ICE Publishing, London, UK.

McLaughlin J, Ocock M, Oldfield A and Trebes B (2015) *Global Risk Assessment and Strategic Planning*. ICE Publishing, London, UK.

Perry P (2003) *Risk Assessment: Questions and Answers*. ICE Publishing, London, UK.

Design

Austin A, Baldwin A, Hammond J *et al.* (2001) *Design Chains: A Handbook for Integrated Collaborative Design*. ICE Publishing, London, UK.

Designers' Guides – series published by ICE Publishing, London, UK.

Neumann E (2014) *Introduction to Sustainable Civil Engineering Design*. Prentice-Hall, Harlow, UK.

Organisation

Bennett J and Jayes S (1995) *Trusting the Team*. ICE Publishing, London, UK.

Coffey V (2015) *Understanding Organisational Culture in the Construction Industry*. Routledge, Abingdon, UK.

Cornick T and Mather J (1999) *Construction Project Teams: Making Them Work Profitably*. ICE Publishing, London, UK.

Naoum S (2011) *People and Organizational Management in Construction* (2nd edn). ICE Publishing, London, UK.

Project and programme management

Barnes PT, Farren R, Haider AD and Wells KP (2015) *Programme Management in Construction*. ICE Publishing, London, UK.

Chartered Institute of Building (2014) *Code of Practice for Project Management for Construction and Development* (5th edn). Wiley Blackwell, Chichester, UK.

Hamilton A (2004) *Handbook of Project Management Procedures*. ICE Publishing, London, UK.

Hamilton A (2010) *Art and Practice of Managing Projects*. ICE Publishing, London, UK.

Lock D (2007) *Project Management* (10th edn). Gower Publishing, Farnham, UK.

Morris PWG (1997) *The Management of Projects*. ICE Publishing, London, UK.

Walker A (2015) *Project Management in Construction* (6th edn). Wiley Blackwell, Chichester, UK.

Health, safety and welfare

Joyce R (2015) *CDM Regulations 2015 Explained*. ICE Publishing, London, UK.

Perry P (2015) *CDM 2015 Questions and Answers*. ICE Publishing, London, UK.

McAleenan C and Oloke D (eds) (2015) *ICE Manual of Health and Safety in Construction*. ICE Publishing, London, UK.

Putsman T and McArthur P (2015) *Practical Guide to Using the CDM Regulations 2015: Teamwork Not Paperwork*. ICE Publishing, London, UK.

Contract strategy

Bower D (ed.) (2003) *Management of Procurement*. Thomas Telford, London, UK.

Madge P, Edwards L and Lord G (1996) *Civil Engineering Insurance and Bonding* (2nd edn). Thomas Telford, London, UK.

Murdoch J and Hughes W (2007) Construction Contracts: Law and Management (4th edn). Taylor & Francis, Abingdon, UK.

Trebes B and Mitchell B (2012) *Managing Reality* (2nd edn) [5 book set]. ICE Publishing, London, UK.

Uff J (2013) *Construction Law* (11th edn). Sweet & Maxwell, London, UK.

Construction management and supervision

Cooke B and Williams P (2009) *Construction Planning, Programming and Control* (3rd edn). Wiley Blackwell, Chichester, UK.

Harris F and McCaffer R (2013) *Modern Construction Management* (7th edn). Wiley Blackwell, Chichester.

Wearne S (1989) *Control of Engineering Projects*. Thomas Telford, London, UK.

Cost planning, project financing and quantity surveying

Boussabaine AH and Kirkham RJ (2004) *Whole Life-cycle Costing: Risk and Risk Responses*. Blackwell, Oxford, UK.

Brook M (2008) *Estimating and Tendering for Construction* (4th edn). Routledge, Abingdon, UK.

Haidar A and Barnes P (2014) *Delay and Disruption Claims in Construction* (2nd edn). ICE Publishing, London, UK.

Kirkham RJ (2014) *Ferry and Brandon's Cost Planning of Buildings* (9th edn). Wiley Blackwell, Chichester, UK.

Overseas projects

Bennett J (1991) *International Construction Project Management: General Theory and Practice*. Butterworth-Heinemann, London, UK.

Howes R and Tah JMH (2003) *Strategic Management Applied to International Construction*. ICE Publishing, London, UK.

Loraine RK (1992) *Construction Management in Developing Countries*. Thomas Telford, London, UK.

Morgan D (2005) *International Construction Contract Management: An Alphabetical Reference Guide*. Gower, Farnham, UK.

Professional duties

Armstrong J, Dixon R and Robinson S (1999) *The Decision Makers: Ethics for Engineers*. ICE Publishing, London, UK.

Institution of Mechanical Engineers (2015) Consultancy Information Guide: occasional subject guides for engineers and students. Available at http://www.imeche.org/knowledge/library/guides/consultancy-information-guide (accessed 20 July 2015).

Scott B and Billing B (1998) *Communication for Professional Engineers* (2nd edn). Thomas Telford, London, UK.

Steels HM (1999) *Effective Training for Civil Engineers* (2nd edn). ICE Publishing, London, UK.

Waterhouse P and Steels HM (2015) *Successful Professional Reviews for Civil Engineers* (4th edn). ICE Publishing, London, UK.

Civil Engineering Procedure
ISBN 978-0-7277-6069-2

ICE Publishing: All rights reserved
http://dx.doi.org/10.1680/cep.60692.155

Appendix C
Useful addresses and websites

Institution of Civil Engineers (ICE)
One Great George Street
Westminster
London
SW1P 3AA
www.ice.org.uk

Chartered Institution of Civil Engineering Surveyors (CICES)
Dominion House
Sibson Road
Sale
Cheshire
M33 7PP
www.cices.org

Chartered Institution of Highways and Transportation (CIHT)
119 Britannia Walk
London
N1 7JE
www.ciht.org.uk

Institution of Structural Engineers (IStructE)
47–58 Bastwick Street
London EC1V 3PS
www.istructe.org

Chartered Institution of Building Services Engineers (CIBSE)
222 Balham High Road
London
SW12 9BS
www.cibse.org

Chartered Institute of Building (CIOB)
1 Arlington Square
Downshire Way
Bracknell
RG12 1WA
www.ciob.org.uk

Association for Consultancy and Engineering (ACE)
Alliance House
12 Caxton Street
London
SW1H OQL
www.acenet.co.uk

Permanent Way Institution
5 Mount Crescent
Warley
Brentwood
Essex
CM14 5DB
www.thepwi.org

Association for Project Management (APM)
Ibis House
Regent Park
Summerleys Road
Buckinghamshire
HP27 9LE
www.apm.org.uk

Royal Institution of Chartered Surveyors (RICS)
12 Great George Street (Parliament Square)
London
SW1P 3AD
www.rics.org

Construction Industry Council (CIC)
26 Store Street
London
WC1E 7BT
www.cic.org.uk

Construction Industry Research & Information Association (CIRIA)
Griffin Court
15 Long Lane
London
EC1A 9PN
www.ciria.org.uk

The Major Projects Association
John Eccles House
Robert Robinson Avenue
Oxford
OX4 4GP
www.majorprojects.org

European Construction Institute (ECI)
John Pickford Building
West Park
Loughborough
Leicestershire
LE11 3TU
www.eci-online.org

Institution of Chemical Engineers (IChemE)
Davis Building
Railway Terrace
Rugby
CV21 3HQ
www.icheme.org

Institution of Mechanical Engineers (IMechE)
1 Birdcage Walk
Westminster
London
SW1H 9JJ
www.imeche.org

Chartered Institute of Arbitrators (CIArb)
International Arbitration and Mediation Centre
12 Bloomsbury Square
London
WC1A 2LP
www.arbitrators.org

Chartered Institute of Purchasing & Supply (CIPS)
Easton House
Easton on the Hill
Stamford
Lincolnshire
PE6 3NZ
www.cips.org

Institution of Engineering and Technology (IET)
Michael Faraday House
Six Hills Way
Stevenage
Hertfordshire
www.theiet.org

Royal Institute of British Architects (RIBA)
66 Portland Place
London
WIB 1AD
www.architecture.com

The Royal Town Planning Institute (RTPI)
The Royal Town Planning Institute
41 Botolph Lane
London
EC3R 8DL
www.rtpi.org.uk

The Royal Incorporation of Architects in Scotland (RIAS)
15 Rutland Square
Edinburgh
Midlothian
EH1 2BE
www.rias.org.uk

Civil Engineering Procedure
ISBN 978-0-7277-6069-2

Appendix D
Glossary

Admeasurement – apportioning of quantities or costs. See also *Remeasurement, Valuation, Bills of quantity.*

Adjudication – a way of resolving disputes in construction contracts. The Local Democracy, Economic Development and Construction Act 2009 provides parties to construction contracts with a right to refer disputes arising under the contract to adjudication.

Adjudicator – see *Adjudication*; the person appointed to give a decision on a dispute between the parties to the contract.

Agent – in civil engineering in the UK 'agent' is traditionally the title of a contractor's representative on a site. Many now have the title 'project manager'.

Arbitration – a non-judicial process for the settlement of disputes where an independent third party (an arbitrator) makes a decision that is binding.

Bid – an offer to enter into a contract; such an offer by a contractor to construct a project. Also called a 'tender'.

Bills of quantity (BoQ) – a list of the items and quantities of delivered work to be done for the promoter under a contract, for instance a quantity of concrete placed to a specified quality. An equivalent in some industrial contracts is called a schedule of measured work. See also *Schedule of rates, Unit rates.* In the traditional arrangements a BoQ is normally issued with an invitation to contractors to tender for a project, with a specification and the tender drawings, and the contractors insert their 'rates' (prices per unit quantity) for each item. The rates in the contractors' tenders can then be compared item by item. In what are called 'admeasurement' contracts, payment to a contractor is based on these rates × the final quantities of work done.

BIM – building information modelling. An approach to the coordination and management of design and construction data through enhanced interoperability and collaborative working practices.

CDM – The Construction (Design and Management) Regulations – UK legislation first introduced in 1994, implementing European Commission Directive 92/57/EEC on the minimum safety and health standards for temporary or mobile construction sites. The CDM Regulations were revised in 2007 and a further revision came into force on 6 April 2015.

Client – see *Promoter*.

Conditions of contract – the 'conditions' of a contract means all the important terms of that contract. In civil engineering the words 'conditions of contract' are used to mean sets of contract terms on general matters likely to be required in all contracts for a class of projects. They define the words used, the responsibilities of the parties, procedures, liabilities for damage, injuries, mistakes or failures of contractor or sub-contractors, delays, changes in legislation such as taxation, frustration of contract and termination. They are designed to be used with a specification, drawings, schedules and other documents, which state the particular terms of a contract. They are also called 'general conditions of contract', 'model forms' or 'standard forms'. See also *Terms of a contract*.

Construction management – is used with a special meaning in the USA and the UK to mean the employment by a promoter of a construction manager (see *Management contractor*) to help plan, define and coordinate design and construction, and supervise construction by 'trade contractors'. The trade contractors are engaged by the promoter but act under the direction of the construction manager.

Construction manager – a contractor employed by the promoter to help plan, define and coordinate design and construction and to direct and supervise construction by other 'trade contractors' – see *Trade contractor*.

Consultants – professional advisers on studies, projects, design, management, techniques and technical or other problems.

Consulting engineers – consultants who also design projects and supervise construction, usually in firms of partners and supporting staff.

Contract – an agreement enforceable at law.

Contract price adjustment/fluctuation – a term in some contracts for adjustment of the contract price for the effects of inflation on the costs of labour and materials. Data produced from public records of the increased cost of commodities, labour, fuel and so on can be used to ascertain the amount due in each month's payment. See also *Escalation*.

Contractor – in general a supplier of services; in civil engineering usually a company which undertakes the construction of part or all a project, and for some projects also undertakes design or other services.

The Contractor – the party to a contract, as distinct from any contractor. The word 'the is important in English practice as identifying the particular contractor who ha entered into a contract for a project. The contractor may be a joint venture of two or more companies.

Cost plus – see *Reimbursable contract*.

Dayworks – see *Schedule of rates*.

Defects correction period – see *Retention*.

Defects liability period – see *Retention.*

Direct labour – a promoter's own employees employed on construction, sometimes under the internal equivalent of a contract, otherwise as a service department.

Domestic sub-contractor – a sub-contractor selected and employed by a main contractor, i.e. not nominated by the client.

Early contractor involvement (ECI) – used as an expression to denote a non-traditional procurement route, where a contractor's skills are introduced early into a project to bring design, 'buildability' and cost efficiencies to the pre-construction phase.

The employer – see *Promoter.*

The engineer – a person named in some forms of contract to be responsible for administering that contract, particularly in contracts for construction or for the supply and installation of equipment. Also called project manager under the NEC3 Form of Contract.

The engineer's representative – in the ICC contracts, the formal title for the engineer's representative on site, often called 'the resident engineer' – see also *Supervisor.*

Equipment – machines, services and other systems. 'Contractor's equipment' is defined in some civil engineering contracts to mean things used by the contractor to construct the works, but not materials or other things forming part of the permanent works – see also *Plant.*

Escalation – increases (or decreases) in the costs of labour or materials due to inflation (or recession and deflation). See also *Contract price adjustment.*

Feasibility studies – investigation of possible designs and estimating their costs to provide the basis for deciding whether to proceed with a proposed project.

Firm price – varies in its meaning, but is often used to indicate that a tendered price is offered only for a stated period and is not a commitment if it is not accepted within that period.

Fixed price – usually means that a tender price will not be subject to escalation but it may mean that there is no variations term. NB Like some other words used in contract management, 'fixed price' has no fixed meaning and 'firm price' no firm meaning. What matters in each contract is whether its terms of payment include provisions for changes to the contract price, and what the governing law permits.

Framework contract – a contract commissioned by a promoter for the provision of works or services of indeterminate nature. When specific works requirements are identified a contractor or consultant who has successfully tendered a framework contract will be appointed to undertake the works.

General contractor – a contractor who undertakes the whole of the construction of a project, but usually in turn sub-letting parts of his work to specialist or trades contractors and others as sub-contractors.

Liabilities – legal obligations.

Litigation – the legal process where a dispute is settled or decided through the court or tribunal process often culminating in a trial.

Lump sum payment – used in engineering and construction to mean that a contractor is paid on completing a major stage of work, for instance on handing over a section of a project. Strictly it means payment in a single lump. In practice 'lump sum' is used to mean that the amount to be paid is fixed, based on the contractor's tender price but perhaps subject to contract price adjustment.

Main contractor – similar to a general contractor: a contractor who undertakes the construction of all or nearly all a project, but usually in turn sub-letting parts of his work to specialist or trades contractors and others as sub-contractors.

Maintenance period – older name for 'defects liability period'. See *Retention*.

Management or managing contractor – a contractor employed by the promoter to help plan, define and coordinate design and construction and to direct and supervise construction by other 'works contractors' – see *Works contractor*. The works contractors are engaged by, and act under the direction of, the management contractor.

Main contractor – a main contractor, as distinct from a 'management' or 'managing' contractor and/or a construction manager.

Measurement – calculation of quantities of work for a BoQ or for payment – see also *Remeasurement*.

Mediation – the process where a dispute is settled by a mediator encouraging the parties to come to an agreement by discussion.

Milestone and *planned progress payment* – payment to a contractor in a series of lump sums, each paid upon his achieving a 'milestone' – meaning a defined stage of progress. Use of the word milestone usually means that payment is based upon progress in completing what the promoter wants. Payment based upon achieving defined percentages of a contractor's programme of activities is also known as a 'planned payment' scheme.

Model conditions of contract – see *Conditions of contract*.

Nominated sub-contractor – a sub-contractor usually for specialist work who is chosen by the promoter or the engineer rather than by the main contractor, but is then employed by the main contractor

Named sub-contractor – the process by which the promoter may influence the principal contractor's selection of sub-contractors, without responsibility for performance.

Owner – see *Promoter*.

Partnering – collaborative management of a contract by promoter and contractor to share risks and rewards.

Permanent works – the works to be constructed and handed over to the promoter.

Planned payment – see *Milestone*

Plant – traditionally 'contractor's plant' is defined in civil engineering contracts to mean things used by the contractor to construct the works, but not materials or other things forming part of the permanent works – see also *Equipment.*

Pre-qualification – the process of inviting the consultants, contractors or sub-contractors who are interested in tendering for work first to submit information on their relevant experience, performance, capacity, resources, systems and procedures, and from this information assessing which are qualified to be invited to tender – see also *Qualification.*

Principal – see *Promoter.*

Principal contractor – is appointed by the promoter to control the construction phase of any project involving more than one contractor and is responsible for ensuring compliance with the construction phase plan by all contractors and individuals on construction – usually the main or largest contractor on a site.

Principal designer – is a designer who is an organisation or individual (on smaller projects) appointed by the promoter to take control of the pre-construction phase of any project involving more than one contractor.

Private finance initiative (PFI) – see description in Chapters 2 and 4.

Project – any new structure, system or facility, or the alteration, renewal, replacement, substantial maintenance or removal of an existing one.

Project engineer – the title often used in promoters' and consultants' organisations for the role of an engineer responsible for leading and coordinating design and other work for a project. In some cases this title is used where the role is actually the greater one of project manager as described below.

Project management – sometimes used with the special meaning that the promoter employs an independent professional project manager to help plan, define and co-ordinate the work of consultants and contractors to design and construct a project.

Project manager/promoter's manager – the title increasingly used in promoters', contractors' and consultants' organisations for the role of manager of the development and implementation of a project. The role may have other titles, such as 'project director' for a large project. For smaller projects the role is not necessarily a separate job. The term project manager is also used in various forms of contract to describe the role undertaken by the contract administrator – see also *The engineer.*

The promoter – the 'client' for a project, the individual or organisation that initiates a project and obtains the funds for it. In some contracts the promoter is called 'the employer', in others 'the owner', 'the purchaser' or 'the principal'.

Provisional sums – amounts included in a BoQ for work which is not defined before inviting tenders. The contractor is paid an amount based upon the actual work ordered by the engineer.

Public private partnership (PPP) – see description in Chapter 4.

Punch list – a list of defects to be corrected by a contractor or sub-contractor.

Purchaser – see *Promoter*.

Qualification – commonly used to mean an accomplishment or attribute which is recognised as making a person or an organisation fit to undertake a specified role or function – see also *Pre-qualification* – also used to mean that a tender includes reservations or statements made to limit liabilities if that tenderer is given the contract.

Qualified tender – a tender which includes reservations or statements made to limit liabilities if that tenderer is given the contract – see above.

Rate – price per unit quantity of an item of work. Not used to mean the speed of work.

Reimbursable contract – a contract under which a promoter pays ('reimburses') all a contractor's actual costs of all his employees on the contract ('payroll burden') and of materials, equipment and payments to sub-contractors, plus usually a fixed sum or percentage for management, financing, overheads and profit. This is often called a 'cost-plus' contract.

Remeasurement – calculation of the actual quantities of work ordered on the contractor in order to certify the payment due to a contractor. Remeasurement is also known as 'measure-and-value'.

Resident engineer – see *Engineer's representative*.

Retention (retention money) – a part of the payment due to a contractor for progress with the work which is not paid until he has discharged liabilities to remedy defects for a period after the taking over or acceptance of the works by the promoter. In some contracts this period is called the 'defects correction period' or 'defects liability period'.

Sanctioning – used in civil engineering to mean deciding to invest in a project, and not used to mean punishing.

Schedule of rates – what is called the 'schedule of rates' in some contracts is very similar to a bill of quantities in form and purpose. Contractors when bidding are asked to state rates per unit of items on the basis of indications of possible total quantities in a defined period or within a limit of say $\pm 15\%$ variation of these quantities. In other examples, the rates are to be the basis of payment for any quantity of an item which is ordered at any time, for instance in term contracts for maintenance and minor construction work and 'dayworks' schedules included in a traditional civil engineering contract.

Snagging list – see *Punch list.*

Special conditions of contract – conditions added to a set of model or standard conditions of contract to apply to one promoter's projects.

Specialist contractor – a contractor who limits their work to selected types of work, e.g. piling or building services. They are often sub-contractors to general contractors. See also *Trades contractor* and *Works contractor.*

Standard conditions of contract – see *Conditions of contract.*

Sub-contractor – a contractor employed by a main contractor to carry out part of a project. A sub-contractor is not in contract with the promoter.

Sub-letting – employment of a sub-contractor by a main contractor.

Supervisor – used in the NEC system to mean the person appointed to check that the works are constructed in accordance with the contract – see also *Engineer's representative.*

Target-cost contract – a development of the reimbursable type of contract in which promoter and contractor agree at the start a probable 'target' cost for a then uncertain scope of work but also agree that the contractor will share savings in actual cost relative to the target cost but will be reimbursed less than the total extra costs if the target is exceeded.

Temporary works – items built to facilitate the construction of the works.

Tender – an offer to enter into a contract, such an offer by a contractor to construct a project. Also called a 'bid'.

Term contract – a system in which a promoter invites several contractors to give prices for typical work which is to be carried out if and when ordered at any time during an agreed period ('the term'), usually based upon descriptions of types of work which may be ordered but without quantities being known in advance.

Terms of a contract – all the obligations and rights agreed between the parties, plus any terms implied by law. This is a historical view that is no longer of practical assistance in construing construction and engineering contracts. The importance of the breach of a contract provision (whether described as a 'condition' or a 'warranty') will in many cases depend on the seriousness of the breach. For example, the right to payment would almost certainly have been considered a 'condition' but a few days delay in making payment would be considered less serious by the courts than a repeated failure to perform a relatively less important obligation, for example to provide any relevant information held by the client if in fact the information withheld, had it been disclosed, might have prevented a serious accident that has now occurred.

Trade contractor – a contractor employed by a promoter under a construction management arrangement, see also *Construction management.*

Trades contractor – a contractor who undertakes a class of construction work, for instance electrical installation. Often employed by main contractors as sub-contractors.

Turnkey contract – a contract in which the contractor is responsible for the design, supply, construction and commissioning of a complete structure, factory or process plant.

Unit rates basis of payment – payment at a fixed price ('rate') per unit of work done. In UK civil engineering 'admeasurement' contracts the predicted total amounts of work are usually stated item by item in a BoQ and the contractor is paid the rate for each × actual amount of work done.

Valuation – in building and civil engineering contracts in the UK the process of calculating a payment due to the contractor.

Value engineering – an analytical technique for questioning whether the scope of a design and the quality of proposed materials will achieve a project's objectives at minimum cost.

Variation – a change to the quantity, quality or timing of the works which is ordered by the promoter's representative under a term of a contract.

Working Rule Agreement – terms of employment agreed between one or more trades unions and representatives of the employers of the members of those unions.

The works – what a contractor has undertaken to provide or do for a promoter – consisting of the work to be carried out, goods, materials and services to be supplied, and the liabilities, obligations and risks to be taken by that contractor. It may not be all of a project, depending upon what is specified in a contract.

Works contractor or *work package contractor* – a contractor employed by a management or managing contractor on behalf of a promoter or by a promoter under a construction management contract – see also *Management* or *Managing contractor*.

Works manager – sometimes the title of a main contractor's general foreman.

For other definitions see: Gorse C, Johnson D and Pritchard A (2012) *A Dictionary of Construction, Surveying, and Civil Engineering* (Oxford Quick Reference) (note that some terms in this guide pre-date the CDM Regulations 2015).

vil Engineering Procedure
3N 978-0-7277-6069-2

E Publishing: All rights reserved
tp://dx.doi.org/10.1680/cep.60692.167

ndex